DATE DUE

ILL 5/02/94		ILL: 25405	
GAYLORD			PRINTED IN U.S.A.

BIOPHYSICS

PROGRESS IN PHYSICS A Reprint Series

Volumes to appear in the series:

- Biophysics
- Astrophysics
- Critical Phenomena
- Lattice Dynamics
- Many-Body Problems

Reprinted from
REPORTS ON PROGRESS IN PHYSICS
The Institute of Physics and The Physical Society
47 Belgrave Square, London S.W. 1

BIOPHYSICS

W. FULLER
University of London Queen's College

C. RASHBASS
University of London

L. BRAGG
The Royal Institution, London

A. C. T. NORTH
The Royal Institution, London

W. A. BENJAMIN, INC.

New York Amsterdam

1969

BIOPHYSICS

Library of Congress Catalog Card Number: 70-77747
Manufactured in the United States of America
12345Q32109

The manuscript was put into production on December 23, 1968; this volume was published on March 1, 1969.

W. A. Benjamin, Inc.
New York, New York 10016

Preface

The Institute of Physics and The Physical Society has for many years published the annual volume entitled *Reports on Progress in Physics* which contains some ten to twelve articles on various aspects of physics, written so far as possible so that they are understandable by the physicist who wishes to keep abreast of developments, but is not closely concerned with the subject of the review. Over a period of four or five years several articles on different aspects of the same subject may be included.

In 1968 the Institute and Society decided that there might be a demand for the republication of selected articles from *Reports on Progress in Physics* in the form of paperback and clothbound books. The books would be useful to many physicists wishing to keep abreast of developments but not wanting to buy a complete volume of the *Reports on Progress in Physics* in which possibly only one subject would be of direct interest. The books would also be of value to the new graduate starting on a graduate course in the subject of the books or to a recent graduate starting in a post in which he would need to know the background of the subject.

W. A. Benjamin, Inc., readily agreed to undertake the publication of such a series. The individual papers are reproduced as printed in the original version, but the authors have been given an opportunity to up-date and correct their articles as necessary by supplying addenda and corrigenda for inclusion in the book.

S. F. Edwards, Honorary Editor
Chairman of the Editorial Board
Reports on Progress in Physics

January 1969

Contents*

**The page numbers given here refer to the numbers shown at the foot of each reprint page.*

Physical contributions to the determination of biological structure and function

W. FULLER

Department of Biophysics, University of London King's College, 26–29 Drury Lane, London

Contents

Abstract. Since the Second World War important advances have been made in the understanding of biological phenomena in terms of the detailed three-dimensional structure of the molecules involved and the way these molecules interact with each other. Physicists have made valuable contributions to these developments: firstly in the development of physical techniques for investigating biological structures and secondly in the application of physical concepts and ideas to an analysis of biological processes. The techniques with which this review is mainly concerned are electron microscopy and x-ray diffraction. The application of electron microscopy is illustrated by some recent studies on virus structure where, in the interpretation of the electron micrographs, the high degree of symmetry in the virus particle is used. Recent advances in x-ray techniques are illustrated by describing their use in the determination of protein and nucleic acid structures. In particular the use of isomorphous replacement and anomalous dispersion in single-crystal protein analysis and of Fourier synthesis and automatic refinement techniques in fibre analysis is discussed.

From an analysis of the conformations which have been determined for a number of macromolecules it has been possible to formulate some general principles describing the forces important in defining macromolecular conformation and interaction. Attempts to apply these principles to the prediction of the conformation of other macromolecules are discussed. Many biological structures consist of highly specific aggregates of macromolecules. For the protein coat of simple viruses, principles of efficient design have been formulated to account for the observed structures in terms of identical protein sub-units arranged in approximately equivalent positions.

Recent theories of the control of cellular function are particularly interesting to physicists. Here control appears to be exercised by feedback processes and amplification of the signal is achieved by utilizing the co-operative behaviour of structures constructed from identical sub-units in equivalent positions.

Perhaps the most remarkable contribution of physics to biology has been to emphasize the high degree of order and precision in biological systems. Although to some extent this may have been exaggerated, because many physical techniques are most powerful in dealing with ordered systems, it is very likely that, as for inanimate matter, the ordered state is more common in living things than macroscopic examination might suggest.

1. Introduction

The contribution made by physicists to the understanding of biological problems has been twofold, firstly in the development of techniques for studying biological structures and secondly in the introduction of physical concepts and ideas to the analysis of biological phenomena. These contributions have only been possible because of parallel advances in related subjects (e.g. genetics, physiology and biochemistry), which have enabled particular phenomena to be properly defined and the structures and molecules involved in them to be identified and in many cases isolated for study by physical techniques.

This article is concerned mainly with advances made during the last few years; reference is made to earlier reviews and standard texts which describe previous work. Particular attention is given to those techniques (principally x-ray diffraction and electron microscopy) which provide detailed information on the three-dimensional structure of macromolecules and the way they interact with each other to form regular structures (§§2 and 3). Attempts to predict the conformation of a macromolecule from a knowledge of its chemical structure are reviewed (§4) and also theories which account for the observed structures of simple viruses, and other biological entities with high structural regularity, in terms of the most efficient assembly mechanisms (§5). Finally, the understanding of biological function which has become possible from this structural knowledge is discussed (§6).

Diffraction techniques are most powerful if the structures being studied can be induced to form single crystals or crystalline fibres. In applying knowledge obtained from such studies to biological problems there is the assumption that the structure in the biological environment is similar to that in the crystal. In fact there is considerable evidence that many biological molecules have well-defined three-dimensional structures which, while influenced by changes in their environment, are sufficiently stable for this assumption to be acceptable. This is discussed later with particular reference to small structural changes which are thought to control biological processes (§6).

To physicists perhaps the most striking feature which emerges from a description of biological phenomena in molecular terms is their economy of design. The enormous variety in the appearance and function of living things is in the main achieved by the use of only a small variety of atoms from which are built relatively few types of macromolecule. Biological phenomena can be broken down into a number of basic processes (e.g. storage of energy, synthesis of a particular type of macromolecule) which appear to proceed in a very similar manner in many organisms. Whilst trace amounts of many elements are important biologically, the most commonly occurring atoms are hydrogen, carbon, nitrogen, oxygen, phosphorus and sulphur. The most important macromolecules are the following: the *nucleic acids*, in the chemical structure of which is coded the genetic information which is transmitted from generation to generation and used to control the growth and development of the organism; the *proteins*, in the structure of which the information coded in the nucleic acids is expressed, either as structural features (i.e. the proteins of connective tissue and hair) or as the ability to perform a particular biochemical process (i.e. the storage and transport of oxygen); the *polysaccharides* which as cellulose have structural roles in plants and as starch are used for energy storage; and the *lipids* which are important constituents of the membranes which surround cells and also separate the different regions within a cell. All these macromolecules are polymers built up from a relatively small number of different monomers, usually in a linear array. In nucleic acids the monomer is called a nucleotide, of which there are four commonly occurring types; in proteins it is an amino acid, of which there are twenty different types. The interactions between the various monomers along a polymer chain determine the way it folds up (§ 4). For proteins, which typically contain about 150 amino acids, there are an enormous number of possible sequences and hence three-dimensional structures. A typical cell may need to synthesize many different proteins, but because proteins are linear polymers, the three-dimensional structure of which is determined by their amino-acid sequence, rather than the manner in which they are synthesized, it is possible to produce all the required proteins by a common mechanism. In such molecules the links between successive monomers are identical even though all the monomers are not the same. Therefore with one type of link-forming mechanism and a relatively small number of monomer units an enormous variety of three-dimensional structures can be produced provided that a blueprint is available which defines the monomer sequence. In protein synthesis this blueprint is a nucleic acid (§ 6).

2. Electron microscopy

2.1. *Introduction*

In this and the following section it will be useful to keep in mind the relationship illustrated in figure 1 between an object, its Fraunhofer diffraction pattern and an image of the object. The limit of resolution in the image is proportional to the wavelength of radiation used to observe the object and increases with the solid angle defining the cone of scattered rays collected by L2 and L3. The quality of optical lenses is such that close to the theoretical limit of resolution ($\sim 0{\cdot}2\ \mu$m) can be achieved when an object is observed with light. However, because of the relatively long wavelength of light, this resolution is inadequate by a factor of 100 or 1000 for observing molecular detail in biological structures. Both electrons and x rays have wavelengths within the necessary range and their use has resulted in unique contributions to biological knowledge. However, neither is as convenient to use as light. X-ray lenses are not available and, whilst L1 can be replaced by a system of collimating pinholes or slits and L2 dispensed with by making D so large that all the waves interfering at a particular point on a film at DP are effectively those scattered in the same direction, this only allows the Fraunhofer diffraction pattern to be observed. For an image of the object a lens L3 would be required and therefore if x rays are used the structure of the object must be determined from its diffraction pattern. Recent advances in the study of biological structures by x-ray techniques are discussed in § 3. While electron lenses exist, their numerical aperture for which aberrations are acceptable is so small that the best electron microscopes have a

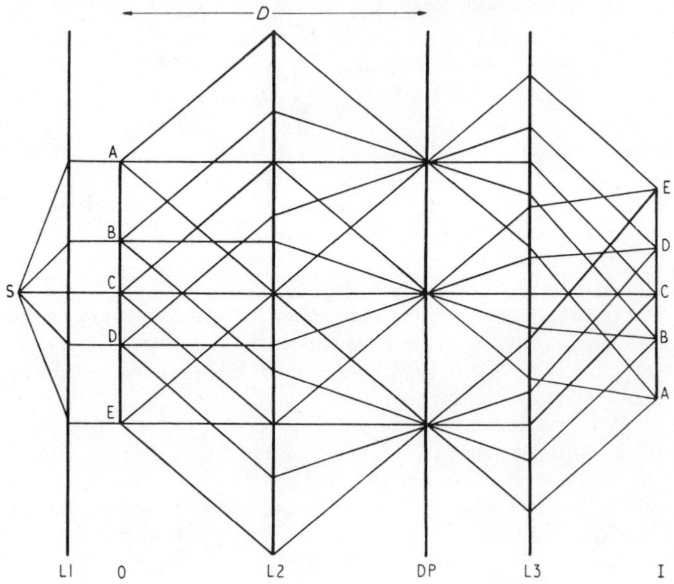

Figure 1. Ray diagram illustrating the relationship between an object O, its Fraunhofer diffraction pattern (at DP) and an image I of the object. L1, L2 and L3 are lenses and S is a point source of illumination. A, B, C, D and E identify corresponding points on object and image.

resolution of only a few ångström units even though the wavelength of the electrons used is about 0·05 Å. However, for biological specimens even this resolution is difficult to attain. This is due partly to the effect of placing the specimen in the vacuum which is essential for the passage of electrons down the microscope, and partly to the uneven distribution of high-electron-density stain which is added to the specimen to increase contrast in the image. During the last six or seven years, a powerful negative-staining technique has been developed in which the objects to be studied are dispersed on a thin carbon film supported on a grid and a heavy metal solution applied which stains the background and runs into interstices of the object. This section describes techniques which have been developed to extract the maximum amount of information from electron micrographs of such objects in those cases where the object consists of a symmetrical arrangement of a number of similar sub-units. This situation occurs quite frequently since, for similar reasons to those which favour macromolecules being constructed by linear arrangement of monomers through identical links, those assemblies of macromolecules which are built by placing similar sub-units in equivalent positions are more efficiently constructed than those which are produced as a giant structure with no internal symmetry (§ 5).

2.2. *Superposition techniques*

Markham *et al.* (1963) were the first to use the symmetry in a biological structure to reduce the background noise in an electron micrograph. The object was a disk-shaped aggregate of protein sub-units from the coat of tobacco mosaic virus. The electron micrograph (figure 2(*a*), plate) suggested that the disk was made up of n similar sectors where n was about 15. Each possible value of n was tested by projecting the micrograph onto a circle of paper which could be rotated about a central axis aligned so that it coincided with the centre of the image of the disk. A piece of photographic paper was mounted on the paper circle and n exposures made on this same piece of photographic paper. Between each exposure the circle was rotated through $360°/n$ and each exposure was $1/n$ that required for image formation with a single exposure. The result of these superimposed images is shown for $n = 16$, 15 and 17 in figures 2(*b*), 2(*c*) and 2(*d*) (plate) respectively; they suggest very strongly that $n = 16$. These workers (Markham *et al.* 1964) have treated electron micrographs of objects with periodicities along their length in an analogous way: successive exposures are taken following translations of the photographic paper parallel to the length of the object by t, $2t$, $3t$, etc., for various values of t; that value resulting in a composite image with the most definition is taken as the fundamental structural repeat in the object. The results of these superposition procedures are often extremely impressive, but as their authors point out the results should be treated with some caution because they are rather vulnerable to the introduction of artefacts into the final image; for example, while figure 2(*b*) is clearly much better defined than either figures 2(*c*) or 2(*d*), both these composite images show more periodicity than the original one.

2.3. *Optical diffraction patterns of electron micrographs*

Klug and Berger (1964) approached the problem of extracting information on the periodicities in an electron-micrograph image in a rather different way. They recorded the Fraunhofer diffraction pattern of the image by using it as the mask in a Lipson optical diffractometer (Taylor *et al.* 1951). Since every point on the micrograph image contributes to each point on the diffraction pattern, measurements on periodicities in this pattern yield average values of corresponding periodicities in the image without time-consuming trial-and-error adjustment of translational and rotational parameters to give the best superposition image. Furthermore, some of the diffraction patterns indicated that the stain was tending to envelop the whole object so that the micrograph image contained features from both the front and back surfaces of the object. Examination of the micrographs themselves also provides evidence for this effect. The type of structure for which such an effect might be studied is indicated by the following example taken from Klug and De Rosier (1966).

They used as an object an orthogonal projection of a helical structure onto a plane through the axis. Two masks were made: in the first (figure 3(*a*), plate) features on both the front and back surfaces of the object were represented, whereas, in the second (figure 4(*a*), plate), only those features on the front surface of the object were represented. Their diffraction patterns are shown in figures 3(*b*) and 4(*b*) (plates) respectively. From a comparison of these patterns it is clear that the diffraction maxima in figure 3(*b*) can be divided into three groups according to the features in the mask which give rise to them: group 1 is due to features on the front surface of the object and enclosed in the rectangular boxes in figure 3(*b*); group 2 is due to features on the back surface of the object and unenclosed in figure 3(*b*); group 3 is due equally to features on the front and back surfaces of the object and enclosed in the central cross in figure 3(*b*). Therefore, if the mask in figure 3(*a*) is placed at O in figure 1 and if a filter is inserted at DP which does not allow any group 2 diffraction maxima to pass and which reduces the intensity of the group 3 maxima by a factor of 2, then the image produced at I should be of the front surface of the object alone without the confusion due to the presence of an image of the back surface as well. That this is in fact the case can be seen by a comparison of figures 3(*c*) and 4(*c*) (plates).

Before this filtering technique can be used to extract an image of one side of a structure from an electron micrograph which is a superposition of images of both sides of the structure, it is necessary to know (or guess) sufficient about the structure to be able to decide which maxima in the diffraction pattern of the micrograph should be filtered out. Furthermore, there are technical difficulties in the filtering process owing to the overlapping of diffraction maxima and the necessity of reducing the intensity of group 3 maxima without altering their phase. This reduction was accomplished by allowing the rays contributing to these maxima to pass through a very fine copper mesh.

Klug and De Rosier (1966) have described the application of this technique to the analysis of electron micrographs from tobacco mosaic virus and bacteriophage tails. The model of tobacco mosaic virus, determined largely from X-ray diffraction studies (see Klug and Caspar 1960 for review), has a surface appearance rather similar to the model illustrated in figures 3(*a*) and 4(*a*). An electron micrograph of a negatively stained particle of tobacco mosaic virus is illustrated in figure 5(*a*) (plate) and its diffraction pattern in the top half of figure 5(*b*) (plate). By examining a large number of such micrographs and their diffraction patterns it was possible to decide which features (indicated by arrows in figure 5(*b*)) in the diffraction pattern were not due to irregularities in the staining or distortions of the true structure. By analogy with figures 3(*b*) and 4(*b*), the differences in intensity of corresponding spots in the right and left halves of the pattern indicate that the contrast due to staining is different for the front and back sides of the virus. A largely one-sided image was obtained (figure 5(*c*), plate), by filtering out those diffraction maxima which originate from the less contrasty side of the object and those due to structural and staining irregularities, i.e. by allowing through only those maxima shown boxed in the lower half of figure 5(*b*). Because the image in figure 5(*a*) was only partially two-sided, reducing the intensity of rays due to both the front and back sides of the object by a copper mesh made little difference to the appearance of the image in figure 5(*c*). The improved definition in the filtered image of the virus can be

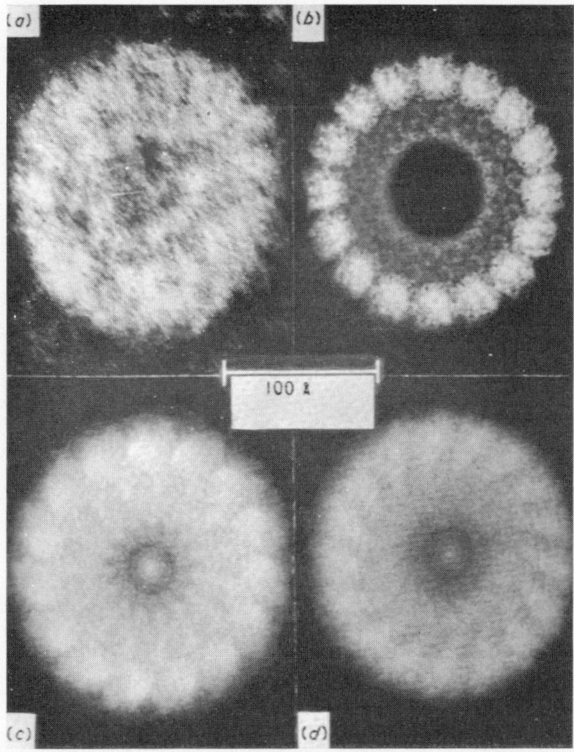

Figure 2. Electron micrograph of a disk-shaped aggregate of protein sub-units from the coat of tobacco mosaic virus. (*a*) is the original micrograph, and (*b*), (*c*) and (*d*) are images produced by the superposition technique described in § 2.2 with $n = 16$, 15 and 17 respectively. (From Markham *et al.* 1963.)

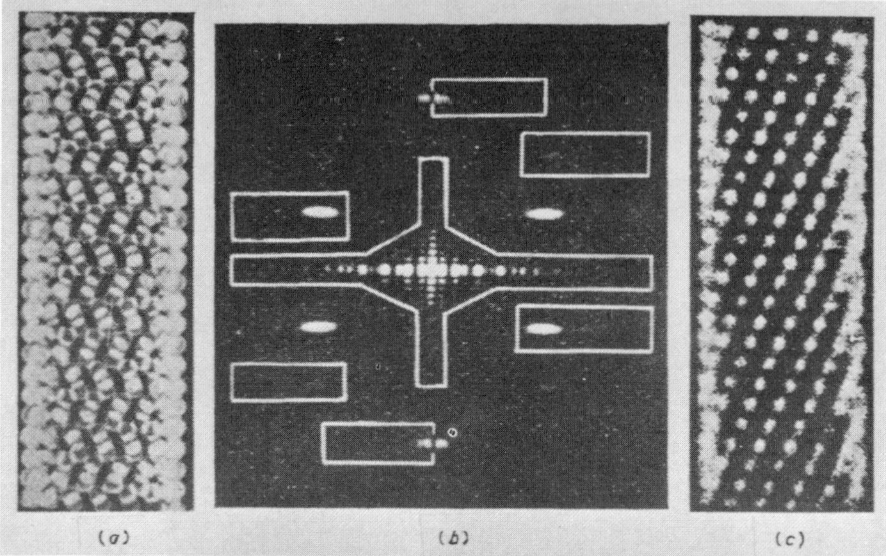

Figure 3. (*a*) Positive replica of a photographic transparency representing the orthogonal projection of a helical structure onto a plane through the axis. (*b*) Fraunhofer diffraction pattern of (*a*) ($\times$ 1·5). (*c*) Filtered image of (*a*), obtained by admitting through the imaging lens (L3 in figure 1) only the diffracted rays enclosed by boxes in (*b*). (From Klug and De Rosier 1966.)

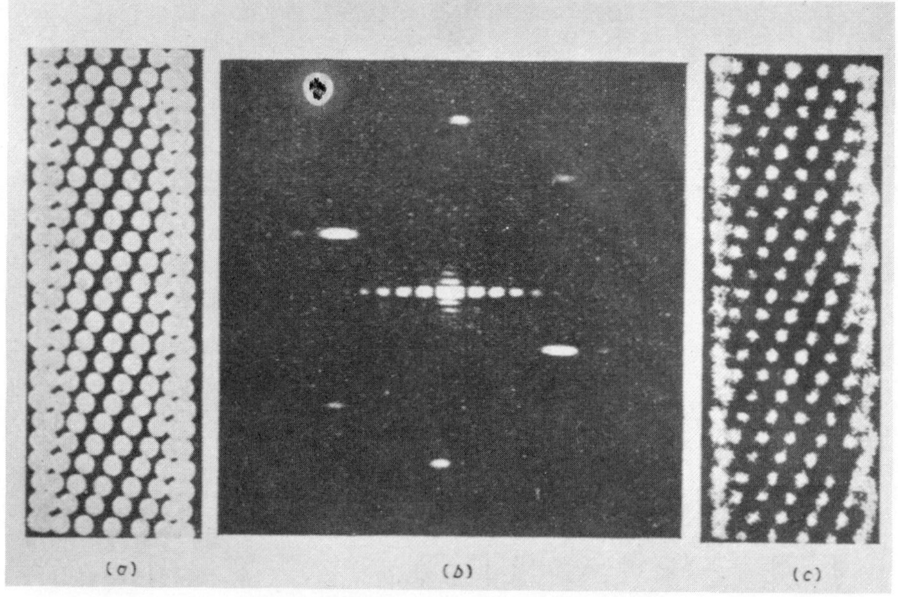

Figure 4. (*a*) Projection of one side only of the helical structure of figure 2(*a*). (*b*) Diffraction pattern of (*a*) ($\times$ 1·5). (*c*) Image of (*a*) without any filtering. (From Klug and De Rosier 1966.)

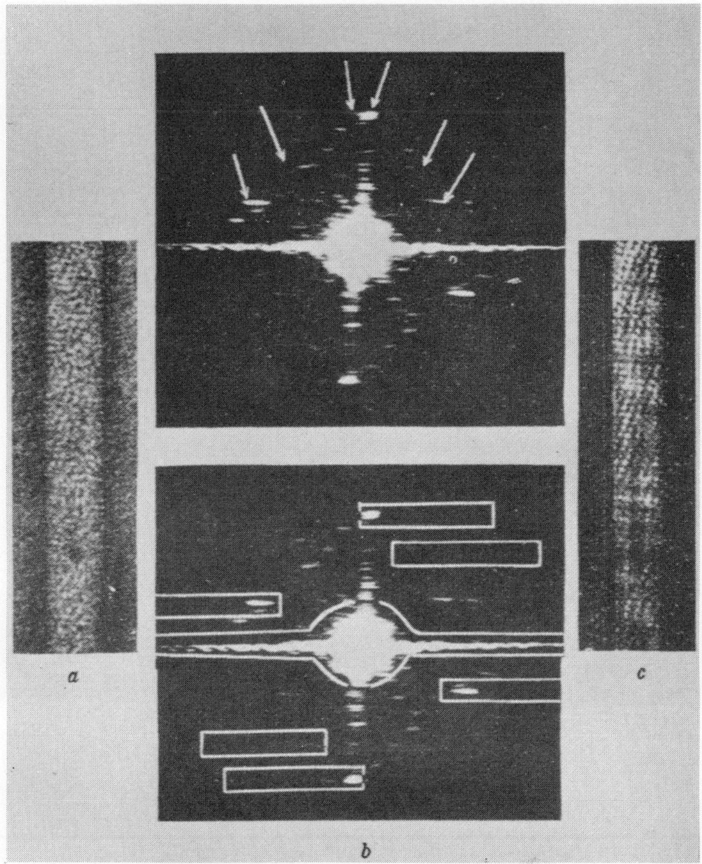

Figure 5. (*a*) Electron micrograph of a negatively stained particle of tobacco mosaic virus. (*b*) Diffraction pattern of (*a*) ($\times$ 1·6). The arrows in the upper photograph indicate the spots which are constant features of the diffraction patterns of tobacco mosaic virus images. The other spots do not recur in all patterns and are attributed to irregularities in the staining and non-systematic perturbations in the particle structure. Differences in the intensity of corresponding spots on left- and right-hand sides of the pattern show that the contrast in the image is largely one-sided. (*c*) Filtered image of (*a*), admitting only the diffracted rays shown boxed in the lower photograph in (*b*). (From Klug and De Rosier 1966.)

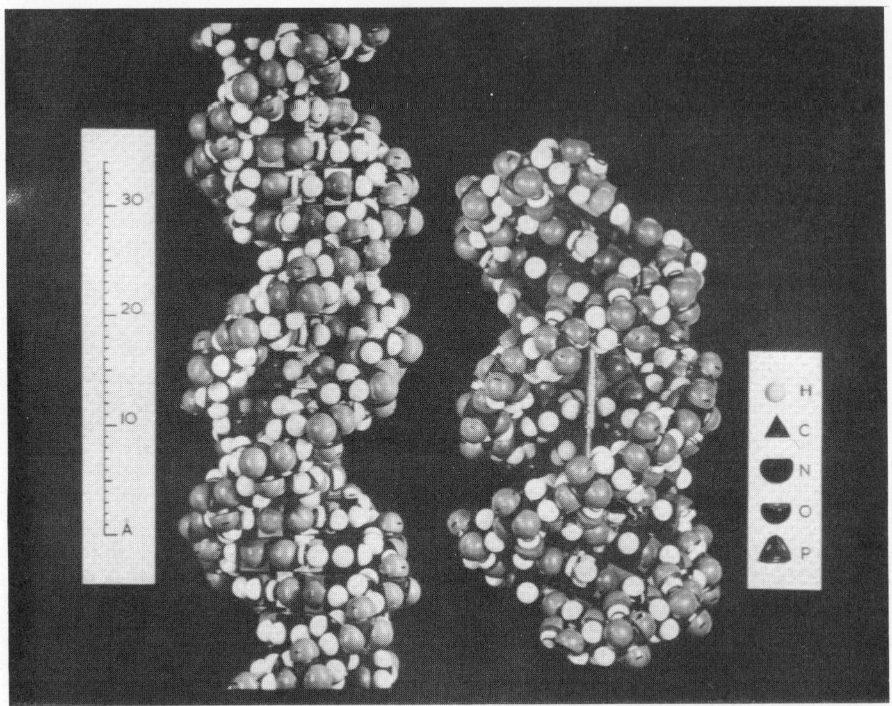

Figure 16. Molecular models of (left) the B conformation of the DNA helix and (right) the RNA helix. The RNA conformation is very similar to that of the A form of DNA.

correlated with information on structural features obtained from X-ray diffraction studies.

There is no doubt that this optical filtering technique will prove very useful in the analysis of electron micrographs of negatively stained objects. However, its use requires a high-quality optical system and considerable experience of diffraction phenomena. For applications of the type described here the diffraction maxima originating from one side of the structure can be distinguished from those originating from the other by recording diffraction patterns from a large number of electron micrographs of the structure. The degree of penetration of the stain on the two sides of the structure will vary from micrograph to micrograph and with it the relative intensity of the two classes of maximum. Nevertheless great care must still be exercised if artefacts of the filtering process are not to be mistaken for structural features in the object.

Caspar (1966) has described a technique for checking models proposed for negatively stained structures. This technique simulates the contrast produced in the electron microscope image by an X-ray radiograph of the model embedded in an X-ray absorbing material. Typically the model is constructed at a scale of 1 cm to 50 or 100 Å from a material (e.g. polyethylene) relatively transparent to X rays, which is coated with an X-ray-dense stain such as barium or calcium sulphate. The relative absorbance of model and stain and hence the contrast in the radiograph can be controlled by varying the X-ray generator voltage (usually in the range 20 to 50 kv). If the model is constructed in two halves, the effect of superposition of images from its front and back sides can be investigated.

Caspar (1966) and Finch and Klug (1966) have described the successful application of this technique in checking models proposed from electron micrographs for human wart virus and turnip yellow mosaic virus. Such checking of models and the investigation of the effect of stain distribution and object orientation on the electron-micrograph image are likely to be the principal uses of this technique. Its use before a fairly satisfactory model for the structure has been obtained is hardly practicable because of the considerable amount of work involved in constructing each model.

3. X-ray diffraction

3.1. *Introduction*

It was pointed out in the previous section that the absence of X-ray lenses requires that structural studies using X rays proceed by analysis of the Fraunhofer diffraction pattern. The intensities of the various diffracted beams can be determined either photographically or by an ionization counter but their relative phases cannot be measured. If they could, there would be no obstacle to replacing lens L3 in figure 1 by a computer and obtaining an image of the object numerically. Before discussing techniques suitable for biological structures which have been developed for generating values for these phases, it is necessary to discuss the types of specimen used in X-ray diffraction studies. Since the X rays scattered by a single molecule are insufficient for a diffraction pattern to be obtained in a reasonable time, studies must be made on arrays of molecules. If all the molecules have an identical orientation and are arranged in a regular three-dimensional array, the X rays scattered by the different molecules will cancel each other out except in certain directions which are determined by the dimensions of the array. The relative intensities of the X-ray beams in these directions depend only on the structure of the individual molecule and not on their three-dimensional arrangement. In a completely analogous way to the assignment of an order number to the various spectra from a linear diffraction grating, the various spectra from these three-dimensional arrays can be distinguished by the values of three indices (h, k, l). The amplitude and phase of the diffraction spectrum (h, k, l) is then given by the structure factor

$$F(h,k,l) = \sum_{j=1}^{N} f_j \exp\{2\pi i(hx_j + ky_j + lz_j)\} \tag{1}$$

where the summation is taken over all N atoms in the molecule and x_j, y_j and z_j are the coordinates of the jth atom expressed as fractions of the lattice vectors **a**, **b**, **c**, which define the molecular arrangement, and f_j is the scattering power of the jth atom in the direction defined by h, k and l. In general $F(h, k, l)$ is complex and may be written as $A+iB$. The diffracted amplitude $|F|$ and phase α are then given by

$$|F| = (A^2+B^2)^{1/2} \tag{2}$$

$$\alpha = \tan^{-1}\left(\frac{B}{A}\right). \tag{3}$$

These expressions can also be applied in the analysis of crystalline fibres. Such fibres are frequently formed by polymer molecules with a helical structure and in them all the molecules have their long axes approximately parallel to the length of the fibre. Certain regions in the fibre called crystallites have neighbouring molecules packed in a regular three-dimensional array. All these crystallites have one crystal axis (conventionally **c** and with a magnitude equal to the helix pitch) approximately parallel, but are in random orientation about this axis. The diffraction from such a fibre is therefore the same as that from a single crystal rotated about its **c** axis during recording of the diffraction pattern. While X-ray diffraction studies of less well-ordered arrays than single crystals and crystalline fibres yield valuable structural information it is always less complete than with crystalline objects. The discussion in this section of recent advances in the X-ray analysis of biological structures is limited to single crystals and crystalline fibres.

The growing availability since the late nineteen-fifties of high-speed electronic computing facilities has stimulated the development and extension of techniques for interpreting single-crystal diffraction patterns to such an extent that for molecules with less than twenty atoms (excluding hydrogen) the analysis has become almost routine. However, the difficulties of the analysis increase rapidly with the number of atoms, so that molecules with a few hundred atoms (other than hydrogen) still present serious difficulties, and the determination of the structure of a molecule containing a few thousand atoms is a major achievement requiring many man-years of experienced crystallographic effort.

3.2. *Structural analysis of globular proteins*

The proteins which form single crystals have a globular shape, and the first two to have their structures determined were myoglobin and haemoglobin by Kendrew,

Perutz and their collaborators (see reviews in Kendrew 1964, Perutz 1963). These workers prepared derivatives of the protein in which groups of high electron density had been attached at a small number of specific sites on the protein without significantly affecting its conformation or mode of packing. To a first approximation the attached groups can be assumed to be scattering against a background of protein scatter and their positions in the crystal determined to a fair degree of accuracy by similar techniques to those used in the solution of crystal structures of small molecules. Using these positions, the contribution in amplitude and phase ($|F_H|$ and α_H) made by the attached groups to the observed structure amplitudes of the derivative $|F_D|$ was calculated for each structure factor using equation (1).

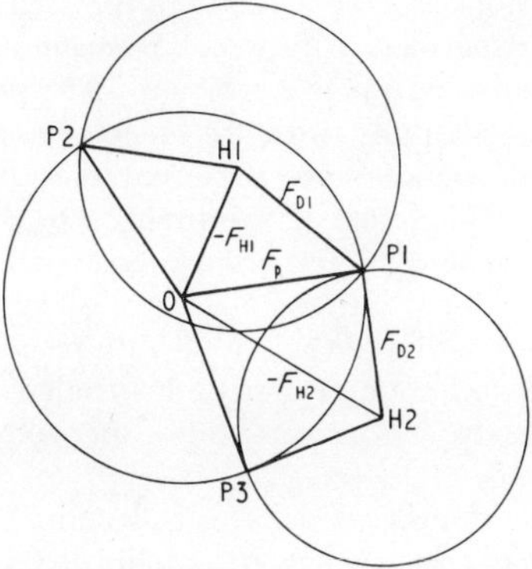

Figure 6. Construction for determining the phase of a protein structure factor knowing the structure factor amplitudes for the protein alone ($|F_p|$) and two isomorphous heavy group derivatives ($|F_{D1}|$ and $|F_{D2}|$) and the contribution in amplitude and phase (F_{H1} and F_{H2}) of these heavy groups to the respective structure amplitudes $|F_{D1}|$ and $|F_{D2}|$. In this construction the amplitude of a structure factor is represented by the length of a vector and its phase by the orientation of the vector in the complex plane. The construction is as follows: (i) with centre O a circle radius $|F_p|$ is drawn; (ii) from O a vector OH_1 is drawn, which represents $-F_{H1}$ in amplitude and phase; (iii) with centre H_1 a circle radius $|F_{D1}|$ is drawn; (iv) the vectors OP_1 and OP_2 which join O to the points of intersection of the two circles represent the two possible descriptions of F_p in amplitude and phase; (v) the construction is repeated for a second derivative to yield two further solutions for F_p; (vi) the solution for F_p (OP_1) which is common to both derivatives is the correct one.

When $|F_H|$, α_H and $|F_D|$ are combined for each structure factor with $|F_p|$, the observed structure amplitude for the protein alone, using the construction in figure 6, two values for α_p, the phase of the protein structure factor, are obtained. Repetition of the process for a second derivative yields two further solutions for α_p and the one which is identical with one of the two found for the other derivative is taken as the correct value. In practice errors in the observed structure amplitudes and in the coordinates determined for the heavy groups make it desirable that more than two derivatives be used, allowing some kind of average α_p to be calculated. The electron density $\rho(x, y, z)$ at any point (x, y, z) in the protein unit cell can then be evaluated by Fourier synthesis using

$$\rho(x,y,z) = \frac{2}{V}\sum_h \sum_k \sum_l |F_p| \cos\{2\pi(hx+ky+lz)-\alpha_p\}. \tag{4}$$

The summation is taken over all the observed structure factors and the process is the mathematical equivalent of that performed by lens L3 in figure 1. The resolution in $\rho(x,y,z)$ increases with the number of terms included in the Fourier synthesis, and for atomic resolution to be achieved all the diffraction spectra corresponding to periodicities in the object of greater than 1 or 2 Å must be included in the summation. By analogy with a linear diffraction grating, where the number of spectra required for a particular resolution increases as the grating spacing increases, the relatively large dimensions of a typical protein unit cell require that many more spectra be recorded and processed to provide an image of the molecule than are needed for a small molecule at similar resolution. The number of spectra which must be included increases rapidly with the degree of resolution required; for example, for sperm-whale myoglobin 400 were required for 6 Å resolution, 9600 for 2 Å, and 25 000 for 1·4 Å. Therefore if a protein is to be determined at atomic resolution high-speed electronic computers are essential. The collection of this quantity of data is also a long and tedious process, and techniques have been developed whereby the orientation of the crystal with respect to the X-ray beam and the position of the ionization counter can be controlled by a computer and the observed diffracted intensity fed directly into the computer (e.g. Arndt and Phillips 1961).

However, even with automatic aids, the collection of sufficient data for an electron-density synthesis of sperm-whale myoglobin at 1·4 Å resolution would have been almost prohibitive if the isomorphous replacement technique had been used. Further, the accuracy in the coordinates of the attached heavy groups is probably inadequate for sufficiently accurate phases to be determined by the isomorphous replacement construction (figure 6) for reflections corresponding to object spacings of less than 2 Å. Therefore an alternative approach was used, in which as many atoms as possible were identified in the 2 Å resolution Fourier synthesis and these used in equation (1) to calculate the amplitudes and phases of all reflections with spacings greater than 1·4 Å. These calculated phases were then combined with the observed amplitudes and the electron-density distribution at 1·4 Å resolution calculated using equation (4). The phases in this summation were deficient because they were calculated using only part of the structure. However, the observed amplitudes were, neglecting experimental errors, completely correct and therefore the resultant image should contain, in addition to the part of the structure already determined, indications of the remainder of the structure. Those indications which most resembled atoms were then included, with the part of the structure used previously, in a calculation of the phases and a new electron-density synthesis. This process can be repeated until new features in the electron-density synthesis cease to appear. Syntheses of a part of the myoglobin structure at 6, 2 and 1·4 Å resolution are illustrated in figure 7.

Many proteins contain atoms of high atomic number (e.g. the iron atoms in haemoglobin and myoglobin) and, as described above, current techniques for protein-structure determination involve the attachment of groups of such heavy atoms to form isomorphous derivatives. Consequently anomalous dispersion effects, which increase in magnitude with the number of electrons in the scattering atom, must be considered. This effect occurs when the wavelength of the incident X rays is close to an X-ray absorption edge for the atom and results in the phase

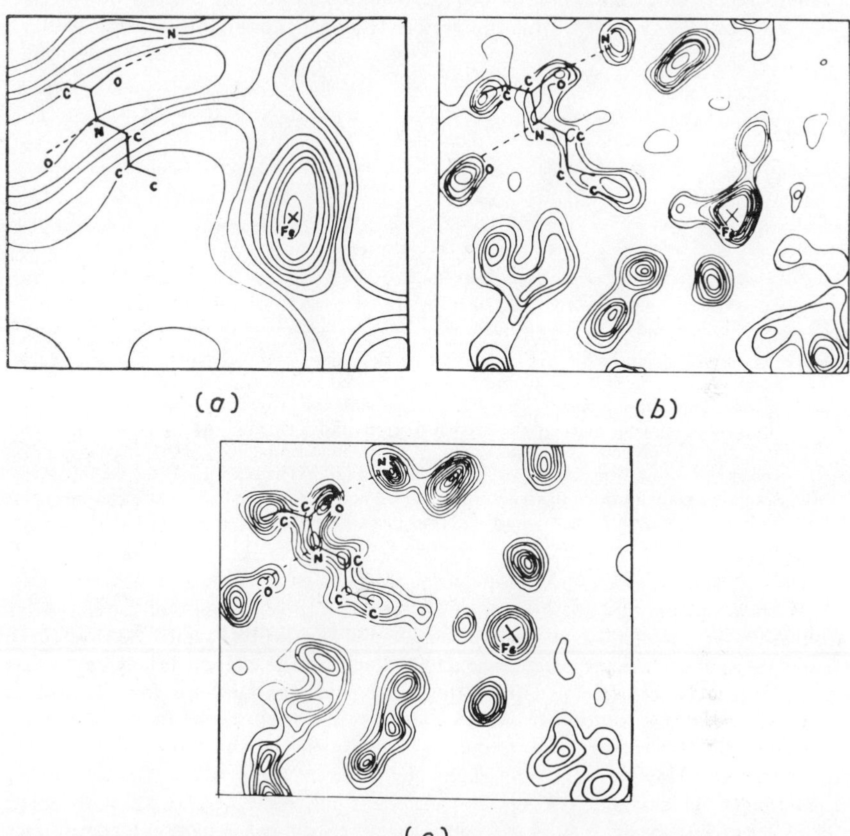

Figure 7. Comparison of the same section through the sperm-whale myoglobin molecule at (*a*) 6 Å, (*b*) 2 Å and (*c*) 1·4 Å resolution. Some atoms are labelled. It should be noted how the 1·4 Å map allows several neighbouring atoms to be resolved. (From Kendrew 1964.)

change of the X rays following scattering being changed from the normal value of π to $\pi - \phi$, where ϕ is a measure of the anomalous effect. In fact this effect has been turned to advantage in phase-determining procedures. The anomalous phase change can be represented in equation (1) by making f_j for this atom complex, i.e.

$$f_j = f_j' + if_j''. \tag{5}$$

The effect of this on $F(h,k,l)$ and $F(-h, -k, -l)$ is illustrated in the vector diagram in figure 8. It can be seen that $|F|$, which in the absence of anomalous scattering is the same for (h, k, l) and $(-h, -k, -l)$ (Friedel's law), is now different. If, as is usual, the position of the anomalous scatterer has been determined and the magnitudes of f' and f'' are known, the constructions in figures 6 and 8 could be combined to yield the phase of $F(h, k, l)$ for the protein, using data from the parent protein alone, only one isomorphous derivative and the knowledge of whether $|F(h, k, l)|$ or $|F(-h, -k, -l)|$ is the greater (Ramachandran and Raman 1956).

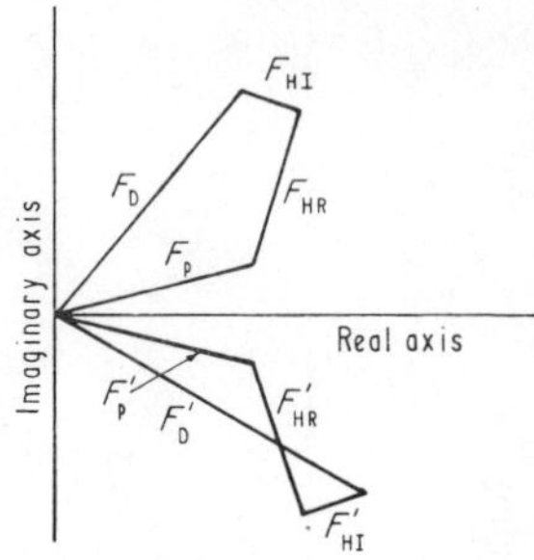

Figure 8. Vector diagram for a Friedel pair of reflections from a structure containing an anomalous scatterer. The diagram shows the real and imaginary axes of the complex plane. The diagram above the real axis represents the structure factor (h, k, l) to which the non-anomalous part of the structure contributes F_P and the anomalous scatterer F_{HR} and F_{HI} on account, respectively, of the real and imaginary parts of its scattering factor (f_j' and f_j'' in equation (5)). From equation (1) it can be seen that the corresponding contributions to structure factor $(-h, -k, -l)$ are the vectors F_P', F_{HR}' and F_{HI}'. (*N.B.* F_P and F_P' are complex conjugates and similarly F_{HR} and F_{HR}'.) Therefore, if f_j'' is non-zero the structure amplitude F_D for (h, k, l) is not equal to F_D', that for $(-h, -k, -l)$.

Ways of using this method in conjunction with a number of isomorphous derivatives of a protein have been discussed by North (1965) and used by Blake *et al.* (1965) in their determination of the structure of the enzyme lysozyme. It has so far only been possible to obtain an electron-density synthesis for the protein haemoglobin at a resolution of 5·5 Å (Cullis *et al.* 1961). Since only the heavier atoms can be identified at this resolution, it is difficult to check the correctness of the structure. However, the anomalous scattering of the iron atoms was used to show that the observed departures from Friedel's law could be accurately accounted for in effectively every case by assuming that the iron atoms have the coordinates indicated by the electron-density synthesis. Inspection of equation (1) shows that in the absence of anomalous dispersion any diffraction pattern can be given by two distinct structures which are related in the following way: for every atom at (x, y, z) in the first structure there is an identical one at $(-x, -y, -z)$ in the second. Therefore the molecular structure determined in the first case is the mirror image of that in the second. These two possible solutions can be distinguished in the presence of anomalous scattering by comparing $|F(h, k, l)|$ and $|F(-h, -k, -l)$ (Bokhoven *et al.* 1951).

From the electron-density synthesis for haemoglobin at a resolution of 5·5 Å (Cullis *et al.* 1962) each of the four sub-units in the molecule can be seen to have a very similar shape to that of the myoglobin molecule at this resolution. The structure of the myoglobin molecule has been determined at a resolution of 1·4 Å (see Kendrew 1964 for a review) and with a knowledge of the amino-acid sequence (Edmundson 1965) it was possible to locate practically every amino acid in the three-dimensional structure. Perutz (1965) has used this detailed model of myoglobin and the amino-acid sequence of haemoglobin (Braunitzer *et al.* 1964) in conjunction with the haemoglobin electron-density synthesis to build a model of the structure in which all the amino acids are located with an accuracy in the atomic positions to the order of 1 or 2 Å.

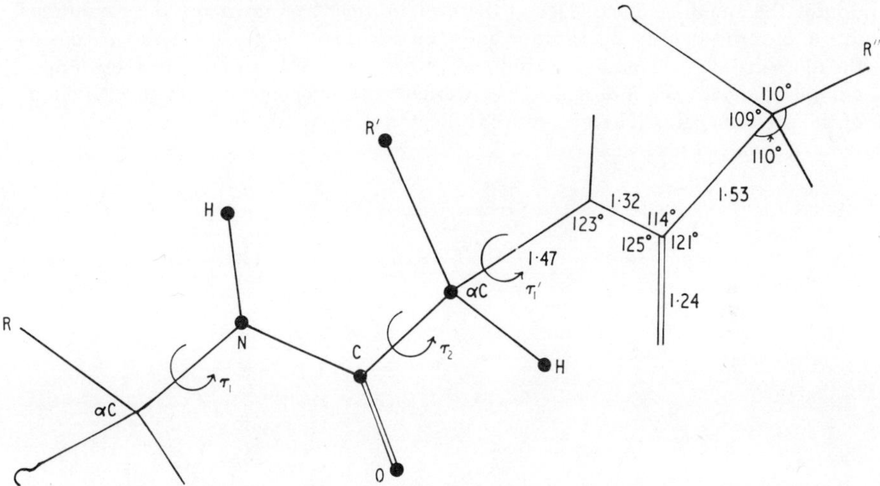

Figure 9. Conformational description of a protein chain. The covalent-bond lengths and angles are as used by Arnott and Wonacott (1966 b) in their refinement of α-poly-L-alanine (see §§ 3.3 and 4.3). R, R′, R″, etc., indicate the positions of the various amino-acid side chains. The NHCO (amide) group is assumed planar and the conformation of the backbone is described by the values of τ_1, τ_1', τ_2, etc. (defined in § 3.2). The amide group is sometimes called a peptide group and proteins referred to as polypeptides.

Implicit in this model-building approach is a great deal of stereochemical data on the geometry of protein chains and the ways in which they can fold up. Diamond (1966) has formalized this approach in a computer-programmed mathematical model-building procedure. The lengths of the covalent bonds linking the various atoms in the protein and the angles between these bonds are assumed to be the same as those in similar chemical groupings in smaller molecules, the structures of which have been determined precisely. These values are shown in figure 9 along with the two single bonds per residue in the protein backbone about which there is free rotation. If this covalent-bond geometry is assumed, the complete three-dimensional structure of the protein backbone can be described as a series of angles (values of the various τ_1 and τ_2) which define the conformation about these single bonds. τ_1 is defined as the dihedral angle between the plane containing atoms R, αC, N and that containing αC, N, C, and τ_2 as the dihedral angle between the planes O, C, αC and C, αC, R′. The conformational angles in the various side chains are defined in a similar way. The number of conformational parameters needed to describe the structure of such a molecule is approximately $\frac{1}{2}N$ where N is the number of atoms other than hydrogen in the molecule; this may be compared with the $3N$ parameters required if the structure is described by the x, y and z coordinates of each atom.

In using this procedure those peaks in the electron-density synthesis which can be identified as corresponding to particular atoms are used as guide points through which the programme threads the protein chain as closely as possible. In order to do this the amino-acid sequence of the protein must be known and the resolution in the electron-density distribution must be adequate for peaks corresponding to the more distinctive amino acids to be identified. The analysis is broken down into a number of parts, each of which is concerned with the conformation of one region of the protein chain. The procedure is illustrated in figure 10.

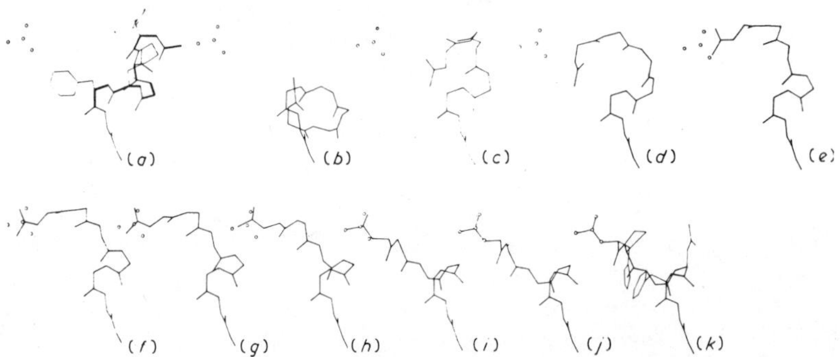

Figure 10. Cycle-by-cycle record of the conformations adopted by a length of protein chain which is required to refold itself so that the free end of the chain comes into coincidence with the guide points shown as open circles on the left of each diagram. There are two peptides at the foot of each figure which do not move; they were guided into those positions and their positions were finalized just before this stage of the calculation was reached. The initial conformation shown in (*a*) is α-helical. The side chains were carried throughout the calculation but for clarity are shown in only the first and last figures. (From Diamond 1966.)

The method has already been used in the interpretation of the electron-density syntheses of haemoglobin, myoglobin and lysozyme. However, as the author points out, if its full potential is to be exploited it will be necessary to incorporate into the refinement procedure stereochemical constraints which will exclude those conformations which are energetically unfavourable. These can arise if atoms which are not covalently bonded together have been brought too close to each other because of the particular single-bond conformations. Attempts to determine the energetically most favourable conformation of a polymer are described in §4.

3.3. *Fibrous structures*

In the refinement procedure just described, the constraints which the X-ray data impose on possible models of the protein are expressed in terms of electron-density peaks obtained by a synthesis of the X-ray data. This is not the normal procedure in X-ray crystallography and was only developed because the number of X-ray spectra and atomic parameters in a protein-structure determination is so large that a conventional least-squares refinement of the atomic parameters to yield the best agreement between observed and calculated diffraction is hardly feasible. However, in the refinement of fibrous structures the situation is quite different. The number of diffraction spectra is usually limited to, at the most, a few hundred. Furthermore, since polymers in crystalline fibres are almost invariably helical, their conformation can usually be described by a relatively small number (say ten or twenty) conformational parameters. Therefore in structural studies of fibrous polynucleotides and polypeptides it is usual to construct scaled skeletal wire models which have covalent-bond lengths and angles with values equal to those observed for similar chemical groups in model compounds and which allow free rotation about the various single bonds (e.g. Langridge *et al.* 1960). The conformation of such models can then be adjusted to give the best agreement between observed and calculated diffraction. Arnott and Wonacott (1966 a) have developed an automatic procedure which performs a least-squares refinement on the molecular-conformational and crystal parameters against the observed diffraction data. Refinement of the molecular-conformational angles (i.e. the orientation about the various single bonds) rather than the (x, y, z) coordinates of individual atoms allows any required values of covalent-bond lengths and angles to be maintained throughout the refinement as in the manual procedure. In addition to allowing refinement of molecular orientation and position within the unit cell this procedure also allows the analysis of statistical structures, i.e. when molecules which exhibit chain sense are pointing randomly up and down in the crystal structure.

The nature of the diffraction data from crystalline fibres is such that the helix pitch is one of the best determined parameters and it is often convenient to keep this length and the number of residues per turn constant during the refinement. The helical symmetry (i.e. the requirement that all the monomers in the helix should have identical stereochemistry) is maintained by means of Lagrange multipliers. The successful application of this procedure to the refinement of terylene (Arnott and Wonacott 1966 a) and to that of α-poly-L-alanine (Arnott and Wonacott 1966 b) suggests that it will be of general applicability in the field of helical polymer refinement, thus providing a more objective procedure for refining models than that involving manual adjustment to obtain the best agreement between observed and calculated diffraction.

The refinement procedure just described can be thought of as taking place in diffraction space. The derivation of the 1·4 Å resolution electron-density-distribution map of myoglobin from the 2 Å map is an example of image refinement. This approach has also been used in the analysis of fibre diffraction patterns, firstly by Marvin *et al.* (1966) and secondly by Arnott (1964, unpublished). Because the amplitudes $|F(h, k, l)|$ used in this summation are completely correct (ignoring experimental errors) the image of the structure calculated by combining these amplitudes with the trial phases will look more like the correct structure than the trial model. Suggestions on how to improve the model can be obtained by subtracting from this image an image of the trial model obtained by combining the phases calculated from the model with the amplitudes calculated from the model. This can be done in one step by combining the difference between the observed amplitude and the calculated one with the calculated phase for each spectrum in the summation of equation (4).

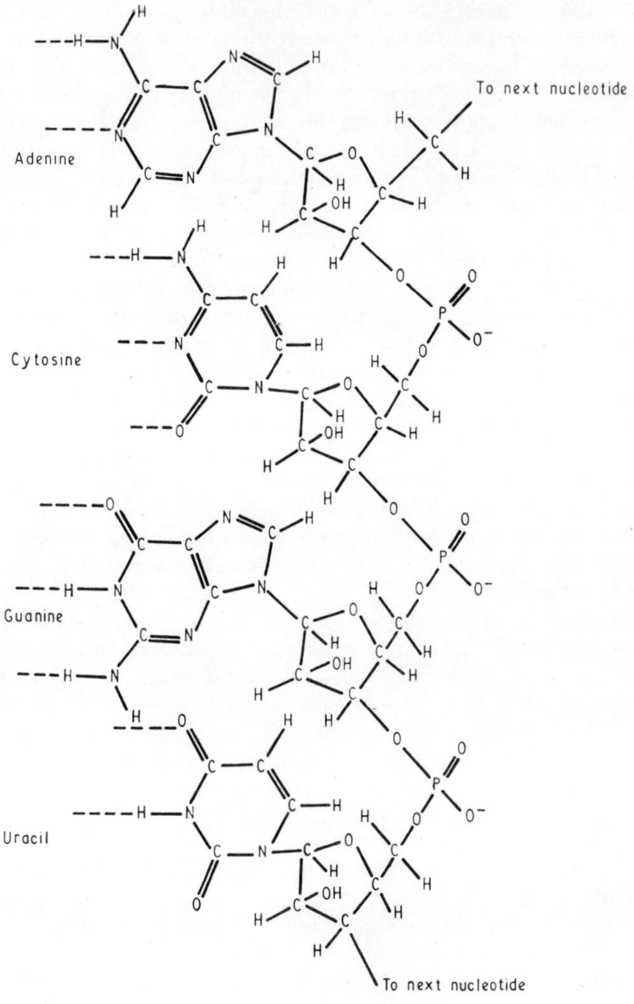

Figure 11. Nucleic-acid chemical structure. All naturally occurring polynucleotides are constructed from nucleotide monomers. Each nucleotide consists of a base (in RNA, usually adenine, cytosine, guanine or uracil) covalently bonded to a five-membered sugar ring which in turn is joined through a CH_2 group to a phosphate (PO_4). Polymerization can be imagined as taking place through covalent-bond formation between the sugar of one nucleotide and the phosphate of another. This figure illustrates the sugar found in RNA. DNA differs in having a sugar in which the OH has been replaced by a hydrogen and also in having thymine (figure 12) instead of uracil as one of the four most commonly occurring bases. The broken lines indicate the direction of the hydrogen bonds formed in Watson–Crick base pairs (see figure 12).

This Fourier difference synthesis can then be used as a guide in refining the model and the whole process repeated until no further improvement in the image can be achieved. This procedure is used in single-crystal analysis for the refinement of atomic positions. The resolution in data from crystalline fibres is rarely adequate to resolve single atoms. Nevertheless in the case of deoxyribonucleic acid (DNA), refinement in the position of groups of atoms was achieved.

The model proposed by Watson and Crick (1953 b) for the structure of DNA was based on the general nature of the x-ray results obtained by Wilkins and his co-workers (Wilkins *et al.* 1953, Franklin and Gosling 1953 a), i.e. that the molecule was helical with a pitch of about 34 Å and an effective diameter of about 20 Å. There are four kinds of nucleotide monomer in DNA (figure 11 illustrates the chemical

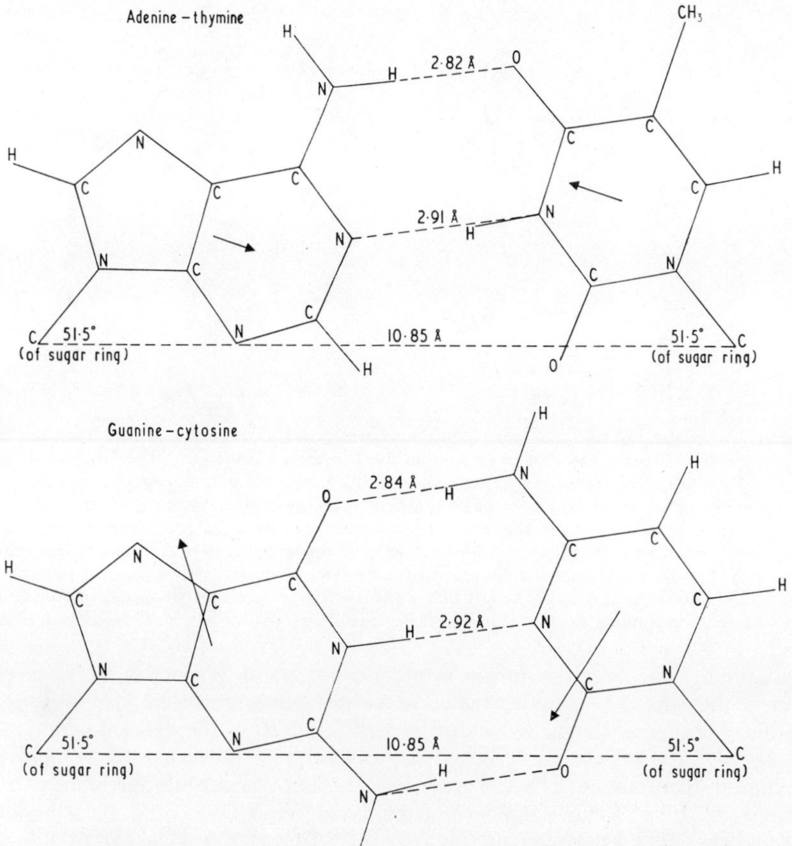

Figure 12. Watson and Crick base-pairing scheme for DNA (refined by Arnott). The arrow in each base represents its permanent dipole moment in magnitude (the length of the arrow) and direction. The broken lines represent hydrogen bonds. (From DeVoe and Tinoco 1962.)

structure of ribonucleic acid (RNA) and the caption describes the small differences in the chemical structures of DNA and RNA). In the structure proposed by Watson and Crick each molecule contained two polynucleotide strands held together by hydrogen bonds between bases in different chains. This base pairing was specific in that adenine was always paired with thymine and guanine with cytosine (figure 12). The base pairs so formed were stacked on top of each other like steps in a right-handed spiral staircase with the sugar–phosphate chains like banisters. The base pairs were perpendicular to the helix axis and there were ten per

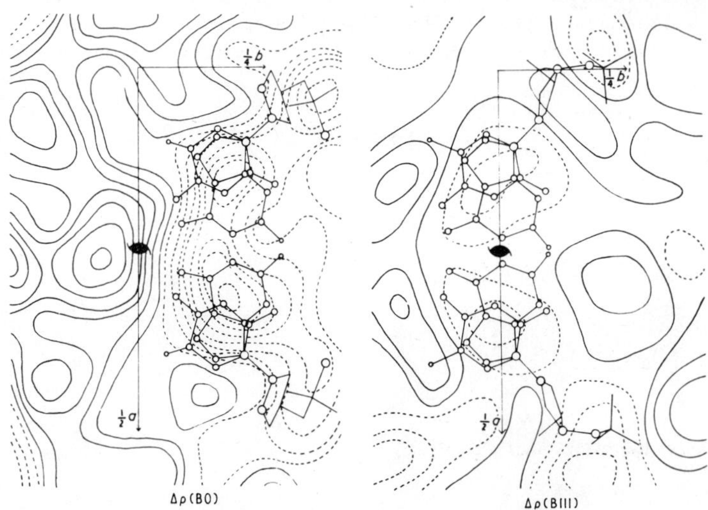

Figure 13. These Fourier difference syntheses correspond to the difference between the true electron density and that in the model used in their calculation. The electron-density distribution is contoured at intervals of 0·1 electrons/Å^3 and negative contours are represented by broken lines. The syntheses were evaluated in the region of a base pair, the position of which in the model is illustrated. In the *left* synthesis the large positive difference near the helix axis (denoted ◆) and the large negative difference in the region of the base pair suggests refinement of the model by movement of the base pairs about 5 Å nearer to the helix axis. The *right* synthesis confirms that such a movement results in a much more featureless difference map. (From Arnott 1964, unpublished.)

helix pitch. The atomic sequence in one polynucleotide chain was the reverse of that in the other. Whilst this model accounted for a great deal of physical and chemical observations and was clearly essentially correct, the detailed comparison of observed and calculated diffraction was unsatisfactory. Because of the enormous biological importance of DNA, a great deal of effort was put into the refinement of the structure by Wilkins and his collaborators (see Wilkins 1963 for a review). Their most refined model (Langridge *et al.* 1960) is in very good agreement with the x-ray data and was obtained by adjustment of skeletal models by the method described previously. One feature of their refinement was movement of the base pairs nearer to the helix axis. Arnott (1964, unpublished) has shown that refinement of the base-pair position could have been achieved by calculating an electron-density-difference synthesis in which the difference between the observed amplitude and that calculated for the Watson and Crick model was combined with phases from this model using equation (4) (figure 13). Similar techniques have been used in the analysis of diffraction data from crystalline fibres of reovirus ribonucleic acid (Arnott *et al.* 1966).

Before concluding this section, one recent advance in X-ray technology should be mentioned. Elliott (1965) has described a focusing toroidal X-ray diffraction camera (figure 14) which gives much greater beam intensity and higher mono-

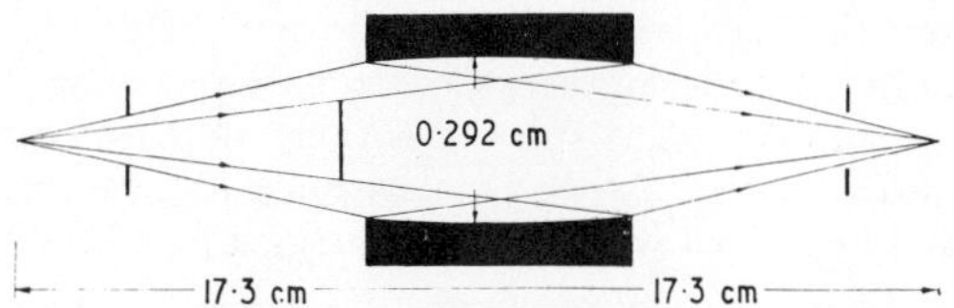

Figure 14. Ray diagram for toroidal or ellipsoidal mirror with apertures and stops for use in the Elliott toroidal focusing camera. The mirror consists of a thin film of gold or nickel on an epoxy-resin casting of a glass rod which had been ground and polished to the correct shape. (From Elliott 1965.)

chromacity than conventional pinhole cameras. Already a number of applications in the study of synthetic and biological polymers have demonstrated its power (Parry and Elliott 1965).

4. Macromolecular conformation

4.1. *General considerations*

In the previous section techniques were discussed for adjusting the conformational angles which define the three-dimensional structure of a polymer to give the best agreement with the diffraction data. If enough were known about the forces defining the interaction of atoms with each other and a molecule with its environment there is, in principle at least, no reason why 'best structures' could not be predicted by procedures which find minimum energy conformations. The nature of these interactions depends on the electronic structure of the atoms involved and therefore any precise description of them must be in quantum-mechanical terms. A complete description in these terms is quite outside the range of current techniques both as regards theoretical formulation and the power of computers available for its evaluation. However, the problem can be approached in a semi-empirical way, in which the wealth of stereochemical data which has been obtained over the past thirty years or so (particularly from X-ray diffraction studies of single crystals and crystalline fibres) is used to formulate a number of stereochemical principles which can be used in predicting the detailed geometry of molecular conformation and molecular interaction. The steps in a conformation-predicting procedure might be summarized as follows.

(i) We determine the *chemical structure* including the absolute configuration at any asymmetric centre; for example, whether an amino acid is the D or L isomer (figure 15).

(ii) We assign values to *covalent bond lengths and angles* in the structure using data from studies on related compounds; for example, the four bonds to the αC of an amino acid (figure 15) make angles of approximately $109\frac{1}{2}°$ with each other.

(iii) We decide which groups in the molecule are rigid; for example, the heterocyclic nucleic acid bases (figure 12) are planar.

(iv) We consider the *hindered rotation* which might be expected about the various single bonds in the molecule; for example, in ethane (C_2H_6) rotation of 60° about the carbon–carbon bond is associated with an energy of 2·8 kcal mole^{-1} (for comparison the energy of a covalent bond is typically between 50 and 100 kcal mole^{-1}). This effect favours the staggering of the hydrogens in one methyl group with respect to those in the other when the molecule is viewed along the carbon–carbon bond. The origin of this effect is still not entirely clear (see Scott and Scheraga (1966) for a recent discussion). As a general rule orientations about carbon–carbon single bonds should be chosen which result in staggering of hydrogens attached to them.

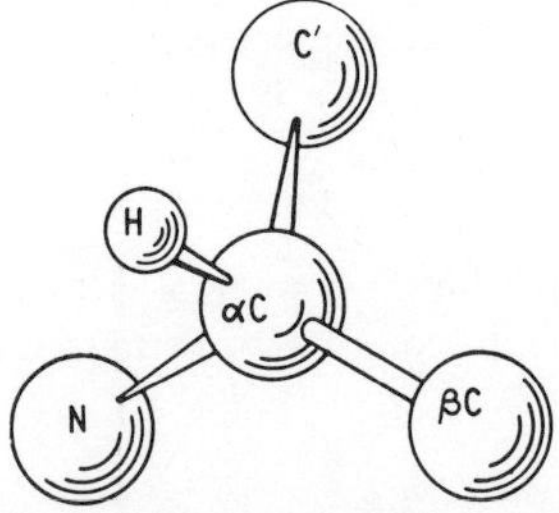

Figure 15. Absolute configuration of groups around the α-carbon in an L-amino acid. In a protein chain βC is the first atom of the side chain, N the nitrogen of the N–H in the amide group on one side of the αC, and C′ the carbon in the carbonyl in the amide group on the other side of the αC. When viewed along the H–αC bond from H to αC, the clockwise sequence of atoms attached to αC is βC, N, C′ for an L-amino acid and βC, C′, N for a D-amino acid. (From Bamford *et al.* 1956.)

(v) Some method of estimating the *van der Waals interaction* energy of pairs of atoms is required. Generally it is convenient to include two effects in this category. Firstly we consider the weak attractive force which every atom has for every other owing to the transient electric dipole in one atom (which is a consequence of its instantaneous electron configuration) polarizing the other atom. The energy of the resultant dipole–dipole attraction varies as $1/R^6$ where R is the separation of the atomic centres. However, if the atoms come too close together the repulsion of the negatively charged electron cloud of one atom by that of the other (this varies approximately as $1/R^{12}$) becomes important. The value of R for which the resultant energy for these two effects is a minimum is taken as the sum of the van der Waals radii of the interacting atoms. While this energy is often only a fraction of a kcal mole^{-1} for each pair of atoms, since it occurs for every pair of atoms, the total van der Waals energy contribution to the stability of a molecular structure can be important. In many organic crystals maximization of the van der Waals stabilization favours close-packed structures and hence accounts for the predominance of those crystal space groups containing symmetry elements which allow closest packing (Kitaigarodski 1961).

(vi) Formal changes and permanent dipoles of atomic groupings in the molecule result in an *electrostatic* contribution to the molecular energy both through interactions with each other and with dipoles which they induce in polarizable groups in the molecule. The energy due to these effects can be quite large (as much as a few tens of kcal $mole^{-1}$) but its value is often rather uncertain because of difficulties in estimating the effective dielectric constant of the medium. Estimates of the magnitude and direction of the permanent dipole moments in the DNA bases are illustrated in figure 12.

(vii) The potential *hydrogen bond donor and acceptor* groups in the molecule should be identified. Whenever a molecule contains a hydrogen attached to an oxygen or nitrogen (referred to as X–H in the following), it assumes a conformation which allows such groups to interact with an oxygen, nitrogen, halogen or sulphur atom (Y in the following discussion) either within the same molecule (*intra*molecular hydrogen bonding) or in another molecule (*inter*molecular hydrogen bonding). This statement is certainly true in crystal structures (Donohue 1952) and is very likely of quite general application. The interaction has very well-defined geometry. The separation of X and Y is characteristic of the atoms involved, i.e. about $2{\cdot}7 \pm 0{\cdot}2$ Å for O–H ... O, $2{\cdot}9 \pm 0{\cdot}2$ Å for N–H ... O, and $3{\cdot}0 \pm 0{\cdot}2$ Å for N–H ... N (see Fuller (1959) for a detailed survey). Also the direction of X- - -Y is always within 15° or 20° of the expected direction of X–H. In crystal-structure determinations hydrogen bonding can be inferred from the length of the X- - -Y contact since, despite the hydrogen between them, the X and Y atoms are slightly closer than the sum of their van der Waals radii. The energy of a hydrogen bond varies with the nature of the donor and acceptor atoms but is of the order of 5 kcal $mole^{-1}$, i.e. about ten times weaker than a covalent bond. Because of their highly directional character and the abundance of oxygen, nitrogen and hydrogen atoms in biological molecules, hydrogen bonds are extremely important in biological function, contributing in particular to molecular recognition processes. Because their energy is comparable with the thermal energy they can be made and broken without disturbing their cellular environment and also without the necessity of enzymes, which are the biological catalysts required for the formation and rupture of the much higher energy covalent bonds.

(viii) Certain atomic groupings are *hydrophobic*, i.e. they tend to aggregate in water solution. The theoretical aspects of this interaction have been considered by a number of workers (e.g. Kauzmann 1959). In simple physical terms it can be visualized as a consequence of the structure of water. In ice each water molecule takes part in four O–H ... O hydrogen bonds, two as a donor and two as an acceptor. These bonds are arranged tetrahedrally about each oxygen atom and their highly directional character leads to a relatively open structure for ice and a lower density than water in which, on average, less hydrogen bonds are formed. As the temperature of water is increased the average number of hydrogen bonds formed per molecule decreases until it eventually vaporizes. However, at room temperature the degree of hydrogen bonding per molecule is still sufficient for the separation of water molecules by the intrusion of groups which cannot form hydrogen bonds (e.g. hydrophobic groups like $-CH_3$ and the top and bottom surfaces of the DNA bases) to be expected to be energetically unfavourable. This discussion suggests that hydrophobic interactions are due to an enthalpy effect. However, studies on model systems suggest that it is primarily an entropy effect. This is possibly because the water surrounding a hydrophobic group is 'frozen' into a relatively ordered structure so that the entropy of the system is decreased. The unfavourable entropy effect can be minimized if hydrophobic groups cluster together. Hydrophobic interactions make significant contributions to the stability of polynucleotides and proteins.

Before describing attempts to predict polymer conformations from these considerations it will be useful to discuss the nucleic acid and protein structures which have been determined by X-ray diffraction from the point of view of the forces stabilizing their three-dimensional structure.

4.2. *Nucleic acid structure*

The Crick–Watson model for deoxyribonucleic acid (DNA) and some details of its refinement against the X-ray data by Wilkins and his collaborators were described in § 3. This conformation is called B (figure 16, plate) and is the one assumed by lithium DNA in crystalline fibres at 66% relative humidity and by sodium DNA in semi-crystalline fibres at 92% relative humidity. The hydrogen bonds linking the bases into pairs (figure 12) have almost perfect geometry (Spencer 1959). The direction and magnitudes of the dipole moments in the four bases are illustrated in figure 12, from which it can be seen that dipole–dipole interactions favour pairing in guanine–cytosine and oppose it in adenine–thymine. DeVoe and Tinoco (1962) have evaluated these interactions and also those due to van der Waals forces and dipole-induced dipole effects. The net energy of formation of a base pair (ignoring solvent effects and hydrogen-bond contributions) is, from these calculations, $+0{\cdot}2$ kcal mole^{-1} for adenine–thymine and $-3{\cdot}9$ kcal mole^{-1} for guanine–cytosine. These authors also calculated the base-pair stacking energy for the 16 different base-pair sequences (guanine–cytosine followed by thymine–adenine is distinguished from cytosine–guanine followed by thymine–adenine, etc.). They assumed that the base pairs were arranged as in the DNA B conformation and included van der Waals, dipole–dipole and dipole-induced dipole terms in their energy summation. The most stable sequence was found to be $\Big\uparrow\begin{matrix}\mathrm{CG}\\ \mathrm{GC}\end{matrix}\Big\downarrow$ and the least stable $\Big\uparrow\begin{matrix}\mathrm{AT}\\ \mathrm{TA}\end{matrix}\Big\downarrow$ where adenine, thymine, guanine and cytosine are abbreviated to A, T, G and C and $\Big\uparrow$ indicates the atomic sequence in the polynucleotide chain, for example figure 11 contains the sequence $\overrightarrow{\mathrm{CG}}$. These calculations are consistent with the observed variation in the stability of the DNA helical structure with its guanine–cytosine content as measured by the temperature required to disrupt the helix (Marmur and Doty 1959). When the DNA is in a fibre at high humidity or in solution, such stacking is also favoured because it maintains the hydrophobic faces of the base pairs in contact whilst still allowing the hydrogen-bonding groups (e.g. $-NH_2$ and $C{=}O$) attached to edges of the bases to interact with surrounding water molecules. The base-pairing scheme described by Watson and Crick has, in addition to near-perfect hydrogen-bond geometry, the sugar-base bonds in identical positions in all four base pairs (guanine–cytosine is distinguished from cytosine–guanine, etc.) and therefore, since the sugar and phosphate groups are identical in each nucleotide

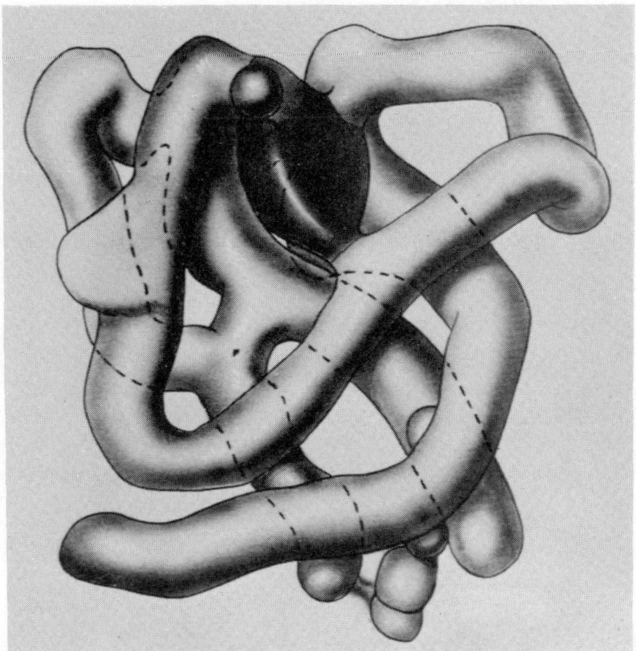

Figure 21. Drawing of a model of the myoglobin molecule at 6 Å resolution. The haem group is shown as a foreshortened dark-grey disk. The small spheres are the heavy groups used in phase determination. Each of the 'sausage-like' structures corresponds to a region of α-helix. The path of a single polypeptide (mainly as α-helix) can be traced with a fair degree of confidence through this model. The subsequent high-resolution analysis of myoglobin (Kendrew *et al.* 1960) showed that the haem group orientation illustrated in this model should be modified by a clockwise rotation of approximately 40° about a horizontal axis in the plane of the disk. (From Bodo *et al.* 1959.)

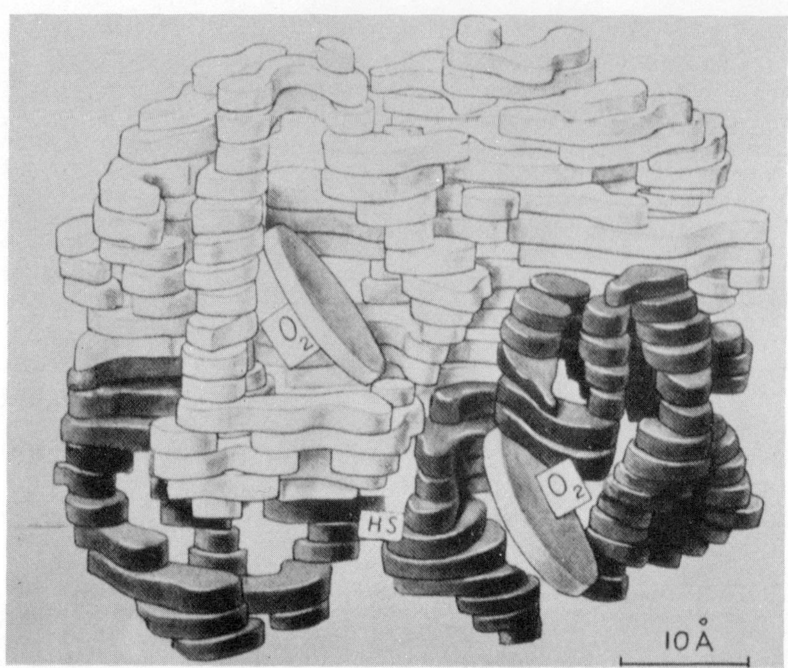

Figure 22. Complete haemoglobin model showing the approximately tetrahedral arrangement of the two pairs of identical sub-units. The haem groups (denoted by disks) in one black and one white sub-unit can be seen. (From Cullis *et al*. 1962.)

Figure 24. A geodesic dome designed by Buckminster Fuller. The surface is made up of quasi-equivalent triangles grouped in hexamers and pentamers about the small rings of the dome. (From Caspar and Klug 1962.)

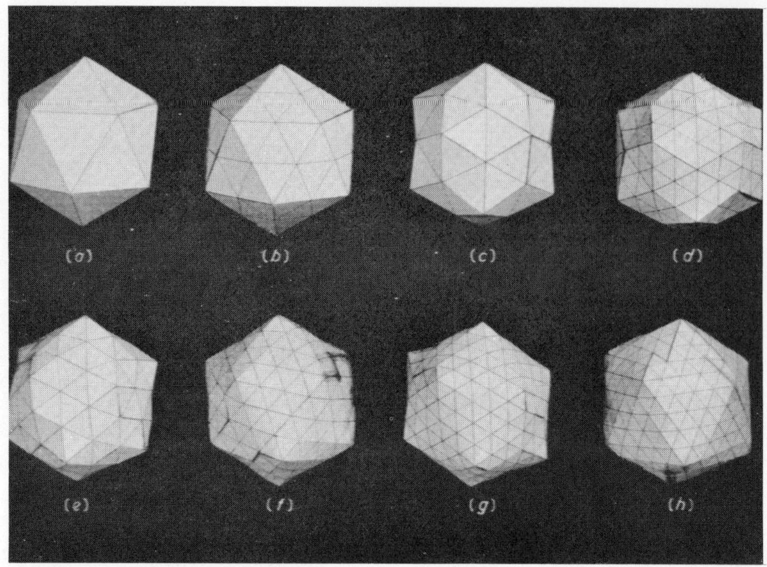

Figure 26. Icosadeltahedra produced by folding a hexagonal net as described in figure 25. (From Caspar and Klug 1962.)

(figure 11), the DNA is able to assume a regular conformation independent of base-pair sequence. When they are studied by X-ray diffraction, nucleic acids are fully ionized with a negative charge on each phosphate group (figure 11). Although to some extent these charges will be neutralized by positively charged metal ions, their mutual repulsion will tend to extend the sugar–phosphate chain so that phosphate–phosphate separations are close to the maximum value of 7 Å. The only way in which this can be achieved, while maintaining the stacking of successive base pairs (thickness 3·4 Å), is by the molecule adopting a helical conformation. The orientations about the various single bonds in DNA and in crystal structures of single nucleotides are generally those which result in staggering of hydrogen atoms.

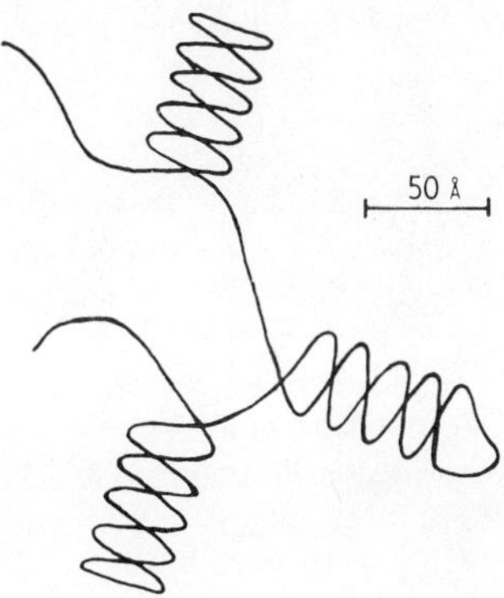

Figure 17. Schematic illustration of the folding up of a part of a single RNA chain to give short double-stranded helices separated by single-strand regions.

When the relative humidity of a sodium DNA fibre is reduced from 92% to 75% the molecules assume a quite different conformation called A (Franklin and Gosling 1953 b, Cooper and Hamilton 1966). This conformational change is reversible and the A form has a similar right-handed double-helical structure with specific base pairing similar to the B form, but the conformation of the sugar–phosphate chains is quite different in the two forms and in A the base pairs are inclined at an angle of 70° to the helix axis (figure 16) (Fuller *et al.* 1965). The A conformation is particularly interesting because it is very similar to that assumed by helical regions of ribonucleic acid (RNA) (Spencer *et al.* 1962). Unlike DNA, where the whole molecule has a two-stranded helical structure, many types of RNA have a less regular structure in which the helical regions are formed by the RNA chain folding back on itself and are separated by single-strand regions (figure 17). Such structures give less well-defined diffraction patterns, and detailed information about the RNA helix only became available firstly when an RNA preparation was enzymatically degraded so that the single-strand regions were eaten away leaving the regular double-helical loops (Spencer *et al.* 1962, Spencer and Poole 1965, Arnott *et al.* 1966), and secondly when a virus was isolated which contained no DNA but whose RNA had a completely regular two-stranded structure (Langridge and Gomatos 1963, Tomita and Rich 1964, Arnott *et al.* 1966, Sato *et al.* 1966). A molecular model of the RNA helix is shown in figure 16. Unlike DNA, RNA helices show no pronounced conformational change with relative humidity; the RNA helix shows a higher thermal stability than DNA helices of similar base composition. Both these effects must be related to the small chemical differences between RNA and DNA (figure 11). However, it is still not clear how these chemical and conformational differences are related. In this context it should be noted that in the model for the RNA helix derived from the x-ray diffraction data (Arnott *et al.* 1966) (figure 16) the hydroxyl group of the sugar does not form a hydrogen bond with a donor atom in the same RNA molecule. The packing of reovirus RNA molecules in crystalline fibres is such that some of the hydroxyls in one RNA molecule are able to form intermolecular hydrogen bonds with a charged oxygen of phosphate groups in neighbouring molecules. The possible biological significance of such interhelix hydrogen bonding is discussed in §6.

4.3. *Protein structure*

X-ray diffraction analysis of proteins was begun in the nineteen-thirties with studies by Astbury and his co-workers on fibrous proteins and by Bernal and Crowfoot on crystalline globular proteins. The success of Pauling and Corey and their colleagues in analysing, in the few years following 1951, the structure of a number of fibrous structures established molecular-model building as an important technique for the determination of macromolecular structure. These workers had initiated a programme at the California Institute of Technology for the precise determination of the crystal and molecular structures of the amino-acid monomers and simple peptides from which proteins are built up. From this programme they obtained information on the covalent-bond lengths and angles to be expected in protein molecules (figure 9), very strong indications that the amide group would not depart significantly from planarity and an appreciation of the importance that hydrogen bonding would be likely to play in protein structure. These stereochemical data were used in the design of molecular models which were then used in a search for stereochemically reasonable conformations of the polypeptide chain in agreement with fibrous-protein x-ray data. Three particularly important structures emerged from this study. Firstly, the α-helix was found (figure 18) (Pauling *et al.* 1951) which accounted for the pattern from the so-called α group of fibrous proteins (e.g. α-keratin) by a helical structure which repeated after eighteen residues and five turns of the helix; the rotation and translation per amino-acid residue were respectively 100° and 1·5 Å. The N–H group in each residue was hydrogen bonded to the C=O of the third residue further along the chain. In this structure the protein backbone formed a tightly packed central core from which the amino-acid side chains radiated like spokes. A left-hand helix of L-amino acids (figure 15) had some steric hindrance if the amino-acid side chain was anything more complicated than that of glycine, i.e. a single hydrogen (table 1) (Huggins 1952). The right-handed helix had good stereochemistry. The second and third protein structures described by Pauling and Corey were the two β conformations (figures 19 and 20) in which the polypeptide chains were extended and lying side by side in sheets (Pauling and Corey 1951). In this case the hydrogen bonds were between neighbouring molecules in the sheet. Since the protein chain has a direction two situations must be distinguished according to whether the chain sense in neighbours is the same (parallel sheet) or opposite (anti-parallel sheet) (see also Huggins 1943). All three of these structures can be described by the atomic coordinates of one amino-acid residue and one or more symmetry elements. They are therefore structures which would be most likely to occur when the amino acids in the protein are sufficiently similar for them to require similar environments. Therefore it might be expected that the most precise data on these arrangements would be provided by

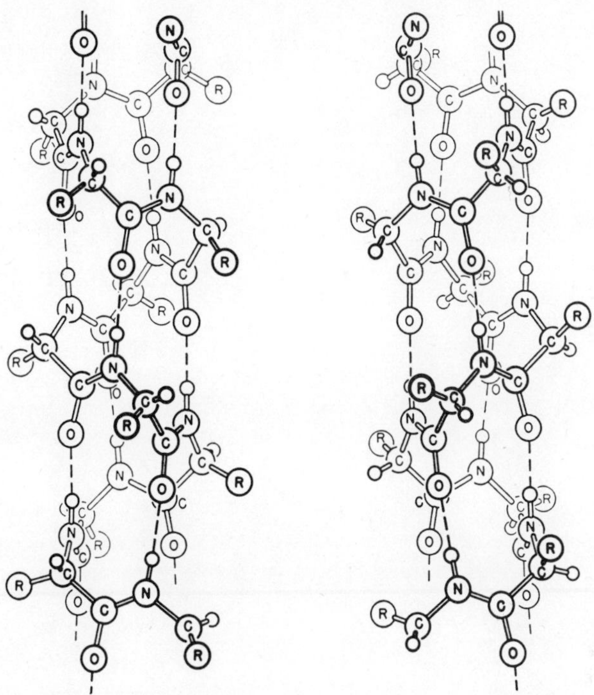

Figure 18. Left- and right-handed α-helical conformations of a protein (polypeptide) chain containing L-amino acids. In proteins (i.e. the naturally occurring polymer) amino acids are invariably L and α-helices right handed. Only the first atom of the amino-acid side chain (R) is shown. (From Pauling 1960.)

studies on synthetic polypeptides in which all the residues are identical. Such a programme has been pursued by Bamford and Elliott and their co-workers (see Bamford *et al.* 1956), and has led to the most complete analysis of an α-helical conformation (Arnott and Wonacott 1966 b). The difficulty with such a study is that, since (unlike two-stranded DNA conformations) both the α and β conformations have a direction, preparation of fibres from synthetic polypeptides is likely to produce statistical structures in which the chains are pointing randomly up and down.

In collagen three polypeptide chains are coiled about a common axis with a translation per residue of 2·9 Å and $3\frac{1}{3}$ residues per turn (Ramachandran and

Table 1. The twenty amino acids commonly found in proteins

Amino acid	Abbreviation	Isoelectric point	Formula
glycine	Gly	6·0	NH_2 (on CH) $H—CH—COOH$
alanine	Ala	6·0	NH_2 (on CH) $CH_3—CH—COOH$
valine	Val	6·0	CH_3 NH_2 $CH_3CH—CH—COOH$
leucine	Leu	6·0	CH_3 NH_2 $CH_3CHCH_2—CH—COOH$
isoleucine	Ileu	6·0	CH_3 NH_2 $CH_3CH_2CH—CH—COOH$
serine	Ser	5·7	OH NH_2 $CH_2—CH—COOH$
threonine	Thr	5·6	OH NH_2 $CH_3CH—CH—COOH$
aspartic acid	Asp	2·8	COOH NH_2 $CH_2——CH—COOH$
asparagine	AspN	—	$CONH_2$ NH_2 $CH_2——CH—COOH$
glutamic acid	Glu	3·2	COOH NH_2 $CH_2CH_2—CH—COOH$
glutamine	GluN	—	$CONH_2$ NH_2 $CH_2CH_2—CH—COOH$
lysine	Lys	10·0	NH_2 NH_2 $CH_2CH_2CH_2CH_2—CH—COOH$
arginine	Arg	10·8	NH_2 NH_2 $CNHCH_2CH_2CH_2—CH—COOH$ ‖ NH
cysteine	CysH	5·1	SH NH_2 $CH_2—CH—COOH$
methionine	Met	5·7	$S—CH_3$ NH_2 $CH_2CH_2—CH—COOH$

Table 1 (cont.)

Amino acid	Abbreviation	Isoelectric point	Formula
phenylalanine	Phe	5·5	$C_6H_5—CH_2—CH(NH_2)—COOH$
tyrosine	Tyr	5·7	$HO—C_6H_4—CH_2—CH(NH_2)—COOH$
tryptophan	Try	5·9	(indole ring)$—C—CH_2—CH(NH_2)—COOH$, with $C{=}CH$, ring N=H
histidine	His	7·6	$N—CH$, HC, $C—CH_2—CH(NH_2)—COOH$, ring N–H
proline	Pro	6·3	CH_2, CH_2, NH, $CH—COOH$, CH_2 (ring)

The chemical formulae of the various amino acids differ only in the side chain. The side chain (R, R′ and R″ in figure 9) is the part of the structure unchanged after the amino acid has been incorporated into a protein chain. Therefore, since the structure of a protein is determined by its amino-acid sequence (§ 4), it is useful to classify the various side chains according to their chemical characteristics (§ 4.1). The side chains of glycine, alanine, valine, leucine and isoleucine are all completely hydrophobic in character. Serine and threonine have one hydrogen-bonding group and may be regarded as having some polar character. The carboxyl group in the side chain of aspartic and glutamic acids is ionized to COO^- at normal pH (see the isoelectric points). These are the two most strongly acidic (negatively charged) amino acids and in a protein would be expected to interact with surrounding water molecules or positively charged groups in the same or neighbouring protein molecules such as the side chains of lysine, arginine and, to a lesser extent, histidine. Lysine, arginine and histidine are the three most strongly basic amino acids. In a number of proteins, the SH groups of two cysteine side chains interact to form a covalent S–S link between the two chains with the elimination of hydrogen. The other sulphur-containing amino acid, methionine, is rather hydrophobic as are the aromatic side chains of phenylalanine, tryptophan and tyrosine. However, the last two also contain hydrogen-bonding groups. In addition to its hydrophobic character proline has one of the hydrogens of its amino group substituted by the tail end of its side chain so that a cyclic structure is formed. The peptide group formed when proline is joined to another amino acid (figure 9) therefore has a substituted NH and cannot take part in hydrogen bonding like that in the α-helix. In globular proteins prolines are always found at the ends of helices or in regions of extended chain.

Kartha 1954, Rich and Crick 1955, 1961, Cowan *et al.* 1955). The three chains are held together by hydrogen bonds but there is still some dispute about the details of the stereochemistry. The proposed models require certain regularities (e.g. a glycine (table 1) as every third residue) in the amino-acid sequence of the protein.

Much of the work described here on fibrous proteins dates from the nineteen-fifties. Since detailed reviews of this work have already been published (e.g. Dickerson 1964), attention in this article has been concentrated principally on those

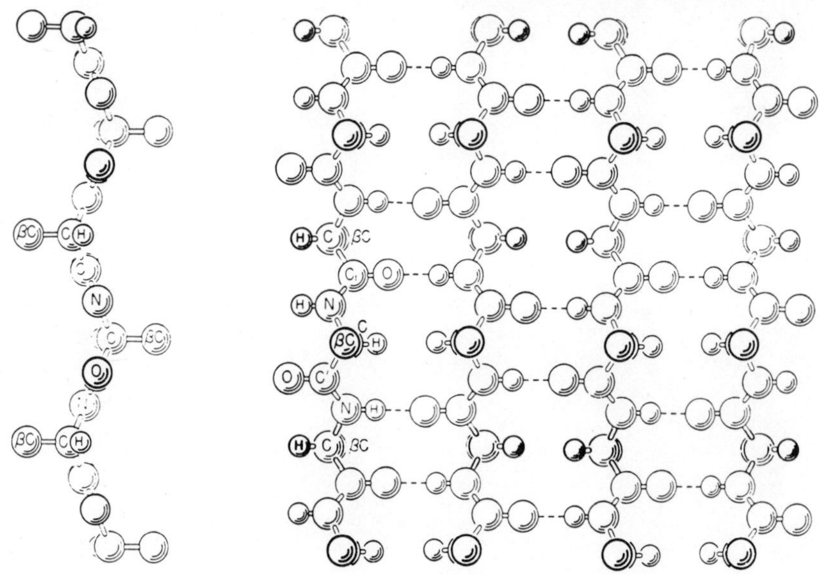

Figure 19. Polypeptide chain arrangement in the antiparallel sheet structure. Only the first atom (βC) of each amino-acid side chain is shown. Hydrogen bonds are represented by broken lines. The isolated chain at the left provides a second view of the molecular conformation, approximately perpendicular to the first. (From Pauling 1960.)

more general aspects of polypeptide structure which are also relevant to discussions of crystalline protein structural studies and techniques for the prediction of protein conformations. In this context it is interesting that the refinement of α-poly-L-alanine (the structure of the alanine side chain is in table 1) by Arnott and Wonacott (1966 b) provides some objective evidence from analysis of a polypeptide structure rather than simple model compounds for the planarity of the amide group, and the helix hydrogen-bond geometry. In their refinement the amide group did not depart significantly from planarity when the orientation about the CN bond (figure 9) was included as a refinable parameter.

Other helical conformations of the polypeptide chain have been proposed (e.g. the γ-helix of Pauling *et al.* (1951)) but they are stereochemically less attractive than the α-helix because of either poorer hydrogen-bond geometry or, as in the case of the γ-helix, which is a rather larger structure with a central hole, poor van der Waals stabilization. While the α-helix is the most frequently observed helical polypeptide chain conformation, related conformations have been observed (e.g. the short region of 3_{10} helix in lysozyme (Blake *et al.* 1965) and the ω-helix in poly-β-benzyl-L-aspartate (Bradbury *et al.* 1962)). In both these cases it appears that interactions between side chains are important enough to distort the backbone conformation. The determination of the structure of the crystalline proteins myoglobin, haemoglobin and lysozyme allows a more detailed analysis of the relationship between amino-acid sequence and protein three-dimensional structure.

Figure 20. Polypeptide chain arrangement in the parallel sheet structure. Only the first atom (βC) of each amino-acid side chain is shown. Hydrogen bonds are represented by broken lines. The isolated chain at the left provides a second view of the molecular conformation approximately perpendicular to the first. (From Pauling 1960.)

Myoglobin was the first protein to have its crystal and molecular structure determined at what was effectively atomic resolution (in fact 1·4 Å). The molecule contains 153 amino acids linked to an iron–porphyrin complex (the haem group) and has the biological function of reversible combination with oxygen. The first three-dimensional Fourier synthesis provided an image of the molecule at 6 Å resolution (Bodo *et al.* 1959). Even at this resolution the general features of the structure were clear (figure 21, plate). This was because there was a large fraction of α-helix in the structure which appeared as rods with a diameter of about 5 Å. The haem group appeared as a disk. Subsequent syntheses with resolutions of 2 Å (Kendrew *et al.* 1960) and 1·4 Å (Kendrew, Watson and Phillips, unpublished), when taken in conjunction with the amino-acid sequence determination (Edmundson 1965), allow the position of every amino acid in the structure to be determined. It might have been hoped that such a determination would have allowed a number of general rules to be formulated which would have been useful in the interpretation of Fourier syntheses of other proteins and in conformation-predicting procedures, for example, which amino acids occur in α-helical regions and which amino acids occur when the helix turns a corner. In fact disappointingly few such general deductions can be made. These are probably limited to the observation that the interior of the molecule is filled with close-packed side chains of the hydrophobic amino acids while the polar hydrophilic amino acids (see table 1 for discussion of amino-acid side-chain character) are on the outside of the molecule where they can interact with solvent molecules and ions which fill the space between molecules.

Like the model for myoglobin, each of the four haemoglobin sub-units (figure 22, plate) has an interior of close-packed hydrophobic amino-acid side chains and polar groups on the surface of the molecule. However, this is achieved despite the quite different amino-acid sequence in haemoglobin and myoglobin.

The haemoglobin model was obtained from an analysis of oxygenated horse haemoglobin. It is clearly of great interest to know what, if any, are the structural changes in the protein following removal of the oxygen. For a number of years it was not possible to obtain suitable crystals of reduced horse haemoglobin (the protein minus the oxygen) and therefore an analysis was made of reduced human haemoglobin (Muirhead and Perutz 1963). This study showed that the loss of the oxygen resulted in movement of the black sub-units (figure 22) so that their separation increased by 7 Å, but with no detectable change in sub-unit conformation. This observation has subsequently been confirmed for reduced horse haemoglobin (Perutz *et al.* 1964). This effect is discussed in §6.

The globin chain conformation (as illustrated in figures 21 and 22) exhibits a remarkable stability both in regard to changes in its environment and changes in its amino-acid sequence (i.e. in solution (Urnes 1963, Ph.D. Thesis, Harvard University), in sperm-whale myoglobin crystals (Kendrew *et al.* 1960), in seal myoglobin crystals (Scouloudi 1960), in crystals of reduced and oxyhaemoglobin from horse (Perutz *et al.* 1964) and in crystals of reduced human haemoglobin (Muirhead and Perutz 1963)).

These similarities, despite the quite different amino-acid sequences in the various globins, can be attributed to evolutionary selection preserving only those mutants which produce proteins which are still functional, for example with the approximate shape of figure 21. Nevertheless it is quite remarkable that such different amino-acid sequences result in such similar conformations. Functional differences between the various globin proteins are demonstrated by the way they interact with each other, for example the specific aggregation of the four sub-units in haemoglobin. The contacts between the like sub-units in haemoglobin (i.e. black and black, and white and white in figure 22) are few and all between amino-acid polar groups (Perutz 1965). In contrast the contacts between unlike sub-units are largely non-polar with a small amount of hydrogen bonding.

Blake *et al.* (1965) have recently described the structure determination of lysozyme, an enzyme which breaks down cell walls. The structural pattern here is similar to that in myoglobin and haemoglobin in that the hydrophobic amino acids are packed in the interior of the molecule with the polar hydrophilic ones on the outside. There are eight cysteine residues (table 1) which form four disulphide links. Crystals have been studied of a complex of the enzyme with various inhibitors, the structures of which are similar to that of the substrate molecule upon which the enzyme acts (Johnson and Phillips 1965). It is assumed that the inhibitor functions by binding to the active site instead of the substrate. These studies revealed the location of the inhibitor and showed that it lay in a cleft in the protein and was linked to it though hydrogen bonds. The position of the bond which is cleaved by the enzyme was located. From a study of the model it appears likely that the side chains of an aspartic acid and a glutamic acid could be the groups responsible for cleaving the substrate.

From preliminary results on other enzymes it appears that something like the cleft in lysozyme may be a common feature of many enzymes. For example, in the 6 Å resolution electron-density map of carboxypeptidase A (Lipscomb *et al.* 1966) there is a depression containing a zinc atom which, from various biochemical studies, is very likely at the active site. Further evidence in support of this depression being the active site is the presence of a pocket near to it which extends into the molecular interior and can accommodate the phenyl group of phenylalanine. Carboxypeptidase A cleaves peptide bonds, and it is interesting that the reaction is favoured if the substrate contains an aromatic side chain like that of phenylalanine in such a position that a model can be built with the side chain penetrating the pocket described above and the bond to be cleaved close to the zinc atom. Therefore, in contrast with lysozyme where the enzyme–substrate interaction appears to be stabilized largely by hydrogen bonds, for carboxypeptidase A the stabilization appears to involve hydrophobic interactions.

From the point of view of the following discussion on the prediction of molecular conformation it is perhaps cautionary to note that, superficially at least, the conformations of both myoglobin and lysozyme appear to be determined by the packing of the hydrophobic side chains within the core of the molecule. Until recently specificity in macromolecular structures tended to be attributed largely to hydrogen bonding rather than to van der Waals and hydrophobic interactions, which were regarded as relatively non-specific interactions.

4.4. *Conformational analysis*

The first attempts to predict the conformation of a polymer chain by calculating the conformational energy as a function of the orientation about the various single bonds were made by De Santis *et al.* (1962, 1963) for polyethylene, polytetrafluoroethylene, polyoxymethylene, polyisobutylene, polyvinylidene chloride and isotactic polypropylene. They assumed that, since these molecules are homopolymers, the only conformations which need be considered are those in which all the residues occupy an equivalent position (i.e. helical structures) and that only the van der Waals interactions make any contribution to the conformational energy. Despite the drastic character of the second assumption and the obvious deficiencies in the expressions for the van der Waals interaction energies for the various atom pairs, the conformations calculated to have the lowest energy corresponded in each case to those observed. The calculations were then extended to polypeptides in which all the amino acids were identical (De Santis *et al.* 1965, Liquori 1966). They predicted that only the α, β and three other helical conformations were sterically permissible and that the α-helix would be distorted by the presence of amino acids with bulky side chains (e.g. valine). These workers (Liquori *et al.* 1966) have extended these calculations by determining the stereochemically allowed values of τ_1' and τ_2 as a function of the amino-acid side chain at R′ (figure 9). These values were then used to predict the structure of the cyclic decapeptide gramicidin S.

Similar calculations to those described by Liquori and co-workers have been carried out by Scheraga and collaborators (Leach *et al.* 1966), Brant and Flory (1965) and Ramakrishnan and Ramachandran (1965). All these workers agree fairly well in their predicted conformations of homopolymers although they differ considerably in the terms included in the energy summations. Scheraga *et al.* (1965) (see also Vanderkooi *et al.* 1966) have predicted a structure for gramicidin S which consists principally of two short lengths of extended β-chain. By contrast the structure suggested by Liquori and co-workers contained two short lengths of α-helix. An X-ray crystallographic analysis of this molecule is in progress.

The similarity in the predictions of the known structures of homopolymers by different workers using rather different terms in their energy summation suggests caution in the acceptance of any results which have been obtained for unknown structures. Nevertheless this is an aspect of macromolecular structural studies in which considerable advances may be expected in the next few years, and even in its present rather limited state of achievement it has proved valuable in emphasizing the importance of determining the stability of structures as well as their geometry.

One interesting application of computers in model building has been described by Levinthal (1966) who suggested that a combination of human brain and computer has a greater chance of success in conformational analysis than the more automatic computer procedures described in the previous paragraphs. A model of the molecule is generated inside the computer and displayed on a cathode-ray tube. The model is constantly rotated so that a three-dimensional impression is given. By allowing the operator to control the molecular-model-building process by the use of a light pen, many functions at which the computer is inherently slow are taken over by a human brain.

5. Self-assembly of biological structures

Viruses are the simplest organisms capable of reproduction. The most rudimentary of them consist only of a nucleic acid packaged in a protective protein coat. Since they lack the synthetic mechanisms required for copying their nucleic acid and translating the genetic material stored in it into protein structure, they can only reproduce by using the mechanisms of a suitable host cell. The molecular interactions involved in such translation and copying mechanisms are described in § 6. Information on the way the amino-acid sequence of a protein determines its three-dimensional structure was discussed in § 4. This section is concerned with the way in which the structure of viruses is related to the efficiency of mechanisms for assembling them from their components.

Many of the smallest viruses, and even some large ones, have simple shapes: either rod like or approximately spherical. Chemical studies have shown that, while the nucleic acid is one long molecule, the protein coat is built up from a large number of identical sub-units. Electron-microscope studies show that the spherical viruses have a 'blackberry-like' appearance and X-ray diffraction studies have given information on the symmetry of these structures and also shown that the rod-like tobacco mosaic virus has a helical structure. The tobacco mosaic virus can be broken down into its protein sub-units and nucleic-acid component by mild alkaline treatment. If the pH is reduced the protein sub-units reaggregate. If the virus nucleic acid is present the reaggregated virus particles are indistinguishable from the original ones, but, even if the nucleic acid is absent, protein assemblies are formed which are similar to those in the virus. Therefore it might be asked if the assembly of virus particles following synthesis of their components in the host cell is a process which proceeds automatically like crystallization, and, further, what arrangements of sub-units within the virus would result in high efficiency for such self-assembly mechanisms.

Crick and Watson (1956) recognized the important principles in simple virus design at a time before all the information on which the previous discussion was based was available. They argued that, on current ideas of the way information on protein amino-acid sequence was stored in nucleic-acid structure, the viral nucleic acid was too small to code for all the virus protein unless there was a repeating structural pattern, i.e. sub-units. They further argued that if such sub-units were identical they would be expected to form arrangements in which they occupied equivalent positions. Clearly the geometry of such arrangements would depend on the three-dimensional distribution of interacting groups on the protein sub-unit. However, there are only a limited number of types of arrangement in which all the sub-units of a structure occupy equivalent positions—based on regular helical and regular polyhedral figures. The equivalence in environment of all the sub-units in a helical structure (ignoring end effects) is obvious and is illustrated in figure 23 by the model of tobacco mosaic virus. Crick and Watson pointed out that strict equivalence in sub-unit environment in polyhedral structures could only be achieved if the sub-units were arranged around the symmetry axes of one of the five regular polyhedra (the platonic solids), i.e. 12 sub-units in a tetrahedron, 24 sub-units in a cube or octahedron and 60 sub-units in a dodecahedron or icosahedron. In fact all the 'spherical' virus structures which have been determined are based on the icosahedron and dodecahedron.

Although the Crick–Watson theory was clearly an essentially correct description of the structures of the small helical and 'spherical' viruses, difficulties became apparent as more information was obtained about the number of sub-units in various 'spherical' viruses and higher-resolution electron-microscope and X-ray diffraction studies were made. These were resolved by Caspar and Klug (1962) who gave a systematic derivation of those structures of the icosahedral type in which all the sub-units were in approximately equivalent positions. Therefore, as in the idealized structures of Crick and Watson, each sub-unit made the same bonds with its neighbours as every other sub-unit, but these bonds were deformed in slightly different ways in different sub-units. This sacrifice of the mathematical concept of exact equivalence for the possibility of building structures from a larger number of smaller sub-units is physically reasonable as long as the distortions are kept small. It is interesting that this solution was inspired by the work of an architect, Buckminster Fuller, who has applied principles of efficient design in building construction (figure 24, plate).

The argument of Caspar and Klug is illustrated in figure 25 which represents a section from an infinite two-dimensional array with hexagonal symmetry. Each motif touches four neighbours. If now a 60° sector is cut from the array with its apex at (0, 0), the array can be folded along the lines through (0, 0) so that the sixfold rotation axis of symmetry at this point is replaced by a fivefold one. The number of other motifs which every motif in the array touches is still four, although

Figure 23. Drawing of a segment of tobacco mosaic virus. For clarity part of the RNA chain is shown without its supporting framework of protein sub-units, but this regular conformation could not be maintained without the protein. Each nucleotide in the RNA is represented by a flat disk. (From Klug and Caspar 1960.)

the interaction geometry has been distorted for contacts along the lines of folding and at the fivefold vertex. However, these distortions are not large and in a real structure may be energetically acceptable. If a further eleven vertices with fivefold rotation axes passing through them are introduced in a similar way at symmetry-related positions in this net, a polyhedron will be produced which is related to a icosahedron. Klug and Caspar have called these figures icosadeltahedra. They can be divided into three groups according to the relative positions of the twelve vertices (figure 25). The first group (figures 26(*a*) and (*b*), plate) includes the regular icosahedron and polyhedra derived from it by dividing each triangular face into $2^2, 3^2, 4^2$, etc., identical equilateral triangles. The second group (figures 26(*c*) and (*d*), plate) includes a dodecahedron on which a regular pentagonal pyramid has been built on each face. The sides of the pyramids are equilateral triangles and further

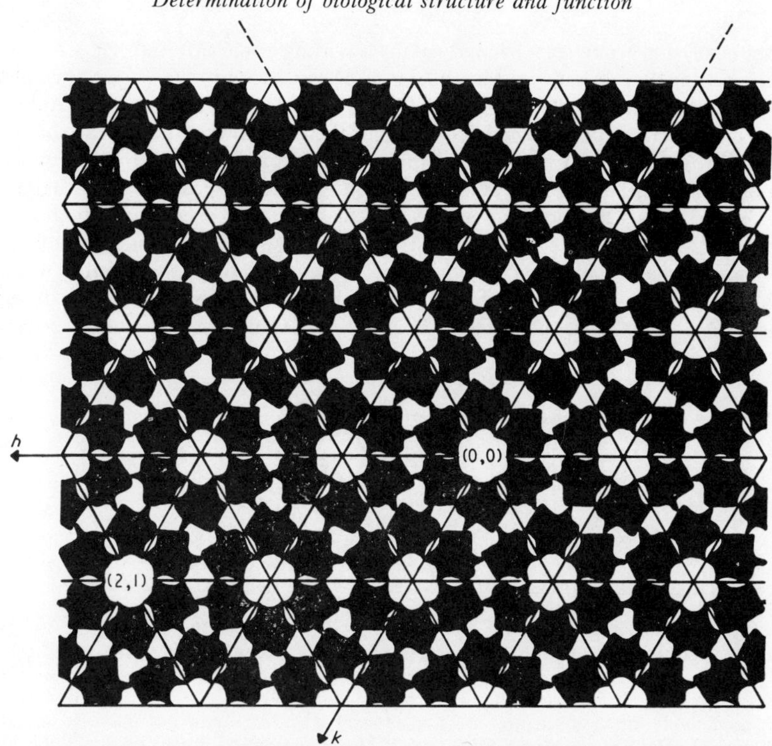

Figure 25. Derivation of the various icosadeltahedra from an equilateral-triangular plane net. The array has sixfold rotation axes of symmetry. Cutting along the broken lines to the point (0, 0) and removal of the sector allows the net to be folded along the lattice lines through (0, 0) so that there is a fivefold rotation axis through (0, 0). Introduction of eleven other fivefold rotation axes at regular positions in the array leads to the formation of an icosadeltahedron. The simplest icosadeltahedra are illustrated in figure 26 and the relation between them and the position of the fivefold axes in this figure is as follows:

Fivefold axes at the following points and symmetry related ones†			Figure produced	No. of faces
(0, 0)	(1, 0)	(0, 1)	26(*a*)	20
(0, 0)	(2, 0)	(0, 2)	26(*b*)	80
(0, 0)	(1, 1)	(−1, 2)	26(*c*)	60
(0, 0)	(2, 2)	(−2, 4)	26(*d*)	240
(0, 0)	(2, 1)	(−1, 3)	26(*e*)‡	140
(0, 0)	(3, 1)	(−1, 4)	26(*f*)‡	260
(0, 0)	(3, 2)	(−2, 5)	26(*g*)‡	380
(0, 0)	(1, 4)	(5, −1)	26(*h*)‡	420

N.B. The section of the lattice illustrated in this figure does not include all the points referred to in the table.

† Coordinate (*h*, *k*) means from the origin O travel *h* units along the *h* axis and then *k* units in the direction of the *k* axis; the point with coordinates (2, 1) is labelled to illustrate this. (0, 0) identifies the origin O.

‡ These are skew structures of which there are right- and left-handed forms. (After Caspar and Klug 1962, Kellenberger 1966 b).

members of the group can be derived by dividing each side into $2^2, 3^2, 4^2$, etc., identical equilateral triangles. The third group (figures 26(*e*), (*f*), (*g*) and (*h*), plate) are skew structures which can exist in left- and right-handed forms. The number of sub-units which can be arranged according to these polyhedral designs so that they are in approximately equivalent environments is three times the number of sides if, as in figure 25, there are three sub-units per side related in position and orientation by a threefold axis through the centre of each face. However, depending on the sub-unit position and the resolution in the image, the number of morphological units may appear, in electron micrographs, to be equal to (i) the number of sub-units, (ii) the number of vertices, (iii) the number of faces, or (iv) the number of edges (figure 27). X-ray diffraction studies indicate that turnip yellow mosaic virus has

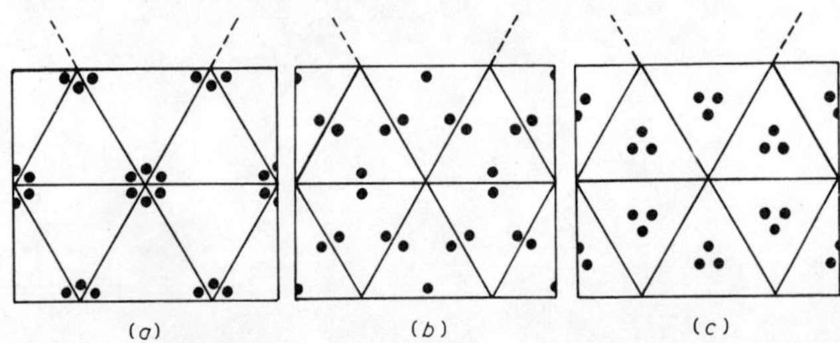

Figure 27. The arrangement of the repeating unit in the plane hexagonal net, which can be imagined as the precurser of the various icosadeltahedra, determines the number of morphological units seen in the electron micrograph, since usually the resolution is inadequate for the structural units to be resolved. The number of observed morphological units will in (*a*), (*b*) and (*c*) be equal to the number of vertices, edges and faces of the icosadeltahedra respectively.

icosahedral symmetry and electron micrographs show a structure with 32 knobs. It can therefore be described by the polyhedron in figure 26(*c*) in which the sub-units are grouped so that it is the 32 vertices of the structure which stand out. This appearance is emphasized because the RNA in the virus shell appears not to be packed as a ball but rather in 32 packets which are deeply embedded in the array of protein sub-units around the fivefold and sixfold axes (Klug *et al.* 1966).

Turnip crinkle virus and tomato bush stunt virus have surface structures which can be accounted for by a polyhedron like that in figure 26(*c*) with sub-units clustered so as to emphasize the mid-points of the 90 edges of the structure. Alkaline degradation of turnip crinkle virus produces, in addition to protein sub-units, structures of the simple icosahedral type (figure 26(*a*)) which appear to form an inner shell constructed out of similar sub-units to the outer one. The tentative suggestion is that the bulk of the RNA in this virus is contained between two concentric protein shells (Klug *et al.* 1966).

Rabbit papilloma virus and human wart virus are DNA viruses in which the bulk of the nucleic acid is contained between an inner protein shell and an outer shell. The structure of this outer shell belongs to the skew polyhedral class (figure 26(*e*)) and it is interesting that the human virus is dextrorotatory while the rabbit is laevorotatory. This presumably reflects some difference in the arrangement of the interacting groups on the surface of the human and rabbit protein sub-units (Klug *et al.* 1966).

While it has only been demonstrated experimentally in a very few cases, it is implicit in the preceding part of this section that the helical and 'spherical' viruses have a sub-unit design which allows them to be formed by a self-assembly process. It is very likely that this is essentially true although, in some cases at least, the nucleic acid or an inner protein core may help to specify the outer shell geometry. A detailed study of the control of assembly of the protein coat of a complicated virus has recently been made by Kellenberger and his collaborators (e.g. Kellenberger 1966 a). This virus has the complicated structure indicated in

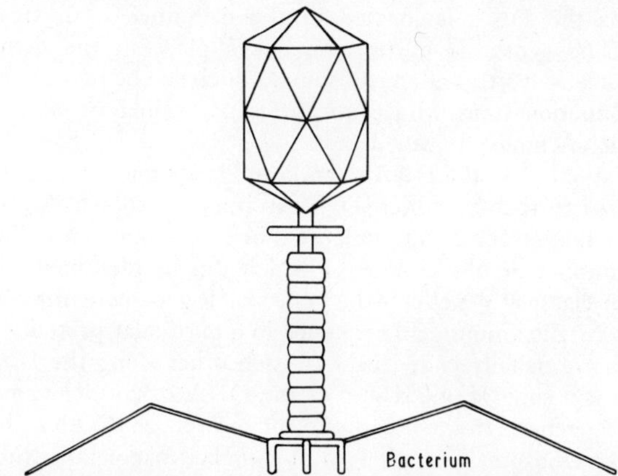

Figure 28. Schematic diagram of a T4 bacteriophage illustrating its structure and the injection of its DNA into a bacterium. (From Kellenberger 1966 b.)

figure 28 and infects the bacterium by injecting its DNA via the long tube. The head of this virus has a polyhedral shape and is built up from sub-units. However, this cannot be an uncontrolled self-assembly process since similar sub-units to those which assembled into the icosahedral end of the head would attempt to close it to form a structure based on a regular icosahedron rather than the prolate one which is observed. It appears that the assembly is controlled by the shape of the DNA and a protein core which is contained in the final head structure.

In this section self-assembly arguments have been developed in terms of virus structure. This is the field for which they were originally formulated and where there is most evidence against which they can be tested. However, there are many other systems where these principles or analogous ones based on similar simple geometrical arguments may be expected to apply.

6. Biological function

The evidence that the genetic information defining an organism's inherited characteristics is stored in its DNA has been extensively reviewed (see e.g. McElroy and Glass 1957). The importance of the Watson and Crick model for DNA was that it showed how this information could be stored in chemical structure (i.e. in the sequence of the four different types of base pair along the DNA helix) and suggested how this information might be copied (Watson and Crick 1953 a). Because adenine is always paired with thymine and guanine with cytosine, the base sequence in each DNA strand contains sufficient information to define the base-pair sequence in the complete molecule. While it is very likely that such a process forms the basis of the DNA replication which precedes cell division and ensures that all the billions of cells in an organism have identical (or at least very similar) information stored in their DNA as that in the single fertilized egg cell from which they are derived, the details of possible mechanisms, in particular the three-dimensional aspects of the unravelling of the parent DNA, have still to be determined. In higher organisms the DNA is located in the cell nucleus in structures called chromosomes. The synthesis of proteins takes place in the cytoplasm which surrounds the nucleus at sites called ribosomes which can be thought of as relatively non-specific production lines whose output is controlled by a blueprint. This blueprint is an RNA molecule called messenger RNA which has a base sequence identical with that of one of the DNA strands and is assumed to be synthesized by a similar mechanism to that by which DNA strands are copied during replication, i.e. by using the other strand as a template. The information stored in the DNA is divided into a number of blocks each of which can be identified with the rather abstract entity of classical genetics—the gene; each gene contains the information necessary to specify the amino-acid sequence in a particular protein. Proteins with related functions are usually coded near to each other along the DNA. A typical messenger RNA is a copy of one strand of the DNA specifying a small number of such neighbouring genes. In the cytoplasm the messenger RNA can be imagined to move through the ribosome like a length of punched paper tape through the tape reader of a computer. Groups of three successive bases in the messenger RNA (called codons) specify each amino acid (table 2). Each codon is recognized (probably largely through base pairing like that in figure 12 (see Crick 1966)) by an anticodon base triplet in another RNA called transfer RNA to which the appropriate amino acid is attached. The codon–anticodon base pairing results in the amino acid being held in the correct position for its attachment to the amino acid which was coded by the previous messenger RNA base triplet. The resultant growing protein chain remains attached to the ribosome until a chain-terminating triplet (table 2) in the messenger RNA is read. There is at least one transfer RNA specific for each amino acid. The mechanism for attachment of the correct amino acid to a particular transfer RNA is still undetermined. After it is released from the ribosome the completed polypeptide folds up in the way discussed in § 4 and is then able to play its structural or metabolic role in the cell's activities.

All the cells in one organism have identical (or at least very similar) information stored in their DNA. However, in higher organisms where extensive differentiation has taken place the various cells have very specialized functions which require only a small fraction of the proteins whose structures are coded in the DNA. Therefore, unless there was a mechanism which controlled the decoding of information from the DNA much of the cell's effort and resources would be wasted in synthesizing proteins it did not need. It has been suggested that this control is exercised by a feedback process (Jacob and Monod 1961). It is postulated that in addition to the structural genes, the transcription of which into messenger RNA and its translation into protein structure were described earlier in this section, there are also regulator and operator genes. It is assumed that the synthesis of messenger RNA can only be initiated at certain points on the DNA molecule. Such an initiating point or *operator* may control the translation of a number of genes which are collectively called an *operon*. The product of a second gene called a *regulator* acts as a repressor by interacting with the *operator* and so blocking initiation of messenger RNA

Table 2. The genetic code

First letter	Second letter: U		C		A		G		Third letter
U	UUU	Phe	UCU	Ser	UAU	Tyr	UGU	Cys	U
	UUC		UCC		UAC		UGC		C
	UUA	Leu	UCA		UAA	Ochre	UGA	?	A
	UUG		UCG		UAG	Amber	UGG	Tryp	G
C	CUU	Leu	CCU	Pro	CAU	His	CGU	Arg	U
	CUC		CCC		CAC		CGC		C
	CUA		CCA		CAA	GluN	CGA		A
	CUG		CCG		CAG		CGG		G
A	AUU	Ileu	ACU	Thr	AAU	AspN	AGU	Ser	U
	AUC		ACC		AAC		AGC		C
	AUA		ACA		AAA	Lys	AGA	Arg	A
	AUG	Met	ACG		AAG		AGG		G
G	GUU	Val	GCU	Ala	GAU	Asp	GGU	Gly	U
	GUC		GCC		GAC		GGC		C
	GUA		GCA		GAA	Glu	GGA		A
	GUG		GCG		GAG		GGG		G

The messenger RNA bases adenine, uracil, guanine and cytosine are abbreviated A, U, G and C. The amino-acid abbreviations are defined in table 1. The ochre and amber triplets almost certainly code for the end of the message; UGA is probably nonsense. It should be noted that the code has high redundancy (i.e. different base-triplets code for the same amino acid) with hardly any meaningless triplets. It should be noted that, because the polynucleotide chain has a direction (figure 11), UGC is distinguished from CGU. (From unpublished abstracts of British Biophysical Society Meeting, December 1966.)

synthesis for this particular operon. In certain systems the repressor appears to be inactive as regards interaction with the operator unless it is complexed specifically with a particular small molecule. Such a system clearly provides the basis of a control mechanism if the small molecule which activates the repressor is a biochemical product of the enzymes which are coded in the operon. If then the small molecule is produced in excess of the cell's requirements, it begins to accumulate and complex with repressor molecules which are then activated so that they can combine with the operator and stop further translation of the operon into messenger RNA. Since messenger RNA in the cell appears to be a relatively labile product, production of the enzymes coded in this operon is halted. This mechanism represents a relatively coarse control of cellular activity. A fine-control mechanism, also based on feedback, which controls the activity of the proteins which are already present in the cell has been suggested by Monod *et al.* (1963). The ability of an enzyme to bind the substrate at its active site is assumed to be affected by the specific binding of a small molecule at another site on the protein. Binding at the second site is assumed to induce a conformational change (an allosteric transition) in the protein which inactivates the site where the substrate is bound. If the molecule which induces the allosteric transition by binding to the enzyme is a product of the biochemical pathway of which the enzyme is a part, then accumulation of this molecule will result in its combination with the enzyme and a halt in the production of the molecule. As the supply of this molecule is exhausted its complex with the enzyme will dissociate and production of the molecule will be switched on again.

Monod *et al.* (1963) have suggested that the repressor which combines with the operator gene in the DNA may be an allosteric protein in which a conformational change is induced by binding of the small molecule whose production is being controlled.

Monod *et al.* (1965) noted that a large number, and probably a majority, of enzyme proteins contain several identical sub-units, for example in haemoglobin two identical α-chains and two identical β-chains (figure 22). Although these sub-units are not linked by covalent bonds the protein aggregate has high stability and the specificity with which the sub-units reassociate even in the presence of other cellular material is extremely high. In both reduced and oxyhaemoglobin (Muirhead and Perutz 1963, Perutz *et al.* 1964) the two α-chains and the two β-chains are related in position by a twofold rotation axis. Monod *et al.* (1965) suggested that such symmetry might be expected to be of general occurrence in proteins built up from sub-units since it conferred a number of evolutionary and functional advantages. Because it contains sub-units in identical positions the protein exhibits co-operative features in its response to changes in sub-unit conformation. This is quite analogous to familiar co-operative phenomena such as melting and freezing of solids. Such systems can be thought of as being finely tuned to a particular chemical or physical impulse and the effect produced on them is so marked that they can be thought of as amplifiers for this particular impulse. For the proteins discussed here, this impulse could be a chance genetic mutation which resulted in a different amino-acid sequence and hence three-dimensional structure for the protein sub-unit. The amplification in the system leads to high discrimination in the evolutionary selection of those mutations which are favoured from the point of view of the protein's function. Alternatively the impulse can be a chemical one such as the binding of oxygen to the sub-unit active site in haemoglobin. The structural changes in haemoglobin associated with removal of oxygen were described in § 4 (figure 22). From both the point of view of molecular conformational analysis as well as the elucidation of biological function it is extremely important to determine how oxygenation can result in such a profound change in sub-unit arrangement with apparently so little change in sub-unit structure.

While from genetic and biochemical studies the genetic code (i.e. the sequence of bases which codes each amino acid) has been determined, the three-dimensional geometry of the molecular interactions involved in the synthesis of messenger RNA and the translation of its base sequence into amino-acid sequence at the ribosomes is largely unknown. This is due largely to a lack of knowledge about the structure of chromosomes, ribosomes and transfer RNA. X-ray diffraction studies of transfer RNA and ribosomal RNA (ribosomes consist of two unequal particles both of which contain one molecule of RNA bound to a number of protein sub-units) indicate that they both contain helical regions with a conformation similar to that described in § 4 for the A form of DNA (Spencer *et al.* 1962, Arnott *et al.* 1966). In ribosomal RNA, these helical regions are probably about one or two turns of the helix long (Spencer and Poole 1965) and separated by a single-strand region of polynucleotide chain so that a part of the molecule has a conformation like that illustrated in figure 18.

For transfer RNA the x-ray structural studies have been supplemented by the following stereochemical considerations. The discussion in § 4.4 of procedures for predicting molecular conformation was restricted mainly to proteins. Similar studies of nucleic acids are rather more formidable for the following reasons:

(i) There are many more single bonds in the polynucleotide than the polypeptide repeat.

(ii) The only polynucleotide structures which have been determined by diffraction techniques are regular two-stranded helical ones. Such studies give valuable information on the geometry of such helical regions but little on the conformation to be expected for those regions of the polynucleotide chain where the nucleotide sequence precludes specific base pairing.

(iii) It is only recently that the nucleotide sequences in naturally occurring nucleic acids have been determined, first by Holley and co-workers (Holley *et al.* 1965) for a transfer RNA specific for alanine, then by Zachau and co-workers (Zachau *et al.* 1966) for two serine specific transfer RNA's and by Madison *et al.* (1966) for a tyrosine specific transfer RNA. Other transfer RNA nucleotide sequences are in the process of determination.

The nucleotide sequences in these three transfer RNA molecules are quite different. However, if each molecule is assumed to fold up in the manner illustrated in figure 29 so that the maximum number of Watson–Crick base pairs (figure 12) are formed, then some interesting homologies between the transfer RNA molecules specific for different amino acids can be seen. All would then have a clover-leaf shape similar to that illustrated for alanine transfer RNA (figure 29) in which the amino acid, anticodon and a number of other common features occur in either similar or identical positions. Such similarities between different transfer RNA molecules are to be expected since they must all be held in the ribosome in a similar way by a mixture of interactions, some of which are specific for the particular transfer RNA like that between codon and anticodon, and others which are non-specific and involve those features which are common to all transfer RNA molecules. It has been suggested (Arnott *et al.* 1966) that the non-specific interactions might include O–H ... O hydrogen bonds (§ 4.1) between ribosomal and transfer RNA helices like those which are thought to exist between molecules of reovirus RNA in crystalline fibres (§ 4.2).

The homologies in the various transfer RNA structures which appeared as a consequence of folding them to maximize the amount of Watson and Crick base pairing suggests that the clover leaf is in fact a basic structural feature of all transfer RNA's. Even if this is so, the three-dimensional structure of the molecule is still largely undefined, since there is considerable flexibility in the way the various arms of the clover leaf can be arranged with respect to each other and also in the conformation of the polynucleotide chain in the non helical loops at the ends of each helical region. However, it is possible that by application of the stereochemical principles outlined in §4 'best energy' conformations for the nucleotides in these loops might be predicted. Such conformations can be tested against physical and chemical studies of transfer RNA (e.g. Feigin and Dembo 1967, Trumanyan *et al.* 1967) and biochemical studies of its function which might be incompatible with certain structures. If a transfer RNA specific for one amino acid could be induced to crystallize, direct determination of its structure would be possible.

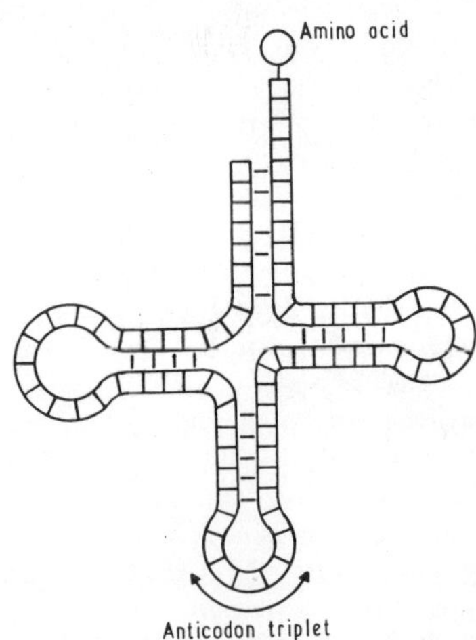

Figure 29. Clover-leaf model for alanine transfer RNA chain in which the RNA has been folded so that the maximum number of Watson–Crick base pairs are formed. Each box represents a base. Bases in Watson–Crick base pairs are linked by a single line. The positions of the anticodon and amino acid are indicated (see Holley *et al.* 1965).

Biological processes are very sensitive to the detailed three-dimensional structure of the molecules involved. For example, a number of small molecules with structures very similar to nucleic acid bases produce errors in the copying and translation of the information stored in nucleic acid. Errors in the copying of the DNA can result in changes in the genetic information which is passed from an organism to its progeny. Such a change is called a mutation and molecules which produce them are called mutagens. Other molecules called carcinogens can produce disruption in an organism's metabolism so that cell division and differentiation are no longer controlled. A number of mutagens, antibiotics and drugs appear to act by forming a complex with DNA. In a number of cases it has been possible to obtain information on the geometry of this interaction by correlation of the results of various physical and chemical techniques with molecular-model-building studies, for example for the mutagen proflavine (Lerman 1961), the antitrypanocidal drug ethidium bromide (Fuller and Waring 1963) and the antibiotic actinomycin (Hamilton *et al.* 1963). Such complexes provide a more complicated system for physical study than the macromolecule alone and models for these interactions are correspondingly less well defined. Nevertheless, the results of such studies are generally consistent with observations on the biological effects of these molecules on intact organisms and provide some hope that, as more is learnt about the molecular basis of biological phenomena, it will be possible to design drugs which will interfere in a specific way with particular biological processes.

7. Conclusions

To the non-scientist it is often surprising to find that substances like sugar and salt, which appear amorphous, have a regular three-dimensional structure. One of the significant developments in biology since the Second World War has been the recognition of order and symmetry in the structure and function of biological systems. This is not to say that biological structures are all highly symmetrical, but from the discussion in the previous sections it is clear that nature frequently exploits the advantages which symmetry confers on a structure, for example the co-operative characteristics which are a consequence of constructing enzymes from identical sub-units related in position by a symmetry axis, and the efficiency which results from constructing viruses from identical sub-units in pseudo-equivalent positions. A second characteristic of biological structures appears to be their stability, for example the conformation of DNA in crystalline fibres appears to be very similar to that of DNA in chromosomes. Again that is not to say that biological structures do not exhibit conformational transformations. In fact such changes are at the heart of some biological processes, for example allosteric control mechanisms. However, it appears that these conformational changes are not a consequence of a poorly defined structure but rather a transition between two well-defined structures. It may be argued that the degree of symmetry and conformational stability which appears to exist in biological structures is exaggerated because two of the most important tools of structure analysis (X-ray diffraction and electron microscopy) are most powerful, and hence have been applied most successfully to structures which have either some internal symmetry or a sufficiently well-defined structure to be crystallized. This dispute will come closer to resolution as structural information is obtained about more and more different types of biological structure. Studies on ribosomes and chromosomes are particularly important in this context. Some support for the idea that biological structures commonly have rather rigid conformations comes from a consideration of molecular interactions. These are frequently highly dependent on the detailed stereochemistry of the molecules involved, for example the activity of an antibiotic is often very sensitive to slight changes in its chemical structure. It is difficult to see how this can occur if the structure is not fairly rigid, since it seems a little implausible to expect interacting molecules to impose the required conformations on each other so that recognition can subsequently take place.

The aim of this article has been to show that biological phenomena are understandable in terms of established physical laws and further that natural selection has favoured those mechanisms which are simple, economical and efficient. Many of these mechanisms find their parallel in techniques devised by man, for example feedback control and principles of efficient design as illustrated in the geodesic dome.

Inevitably an article of this kind must be highly selective. Nothing has been said about electron diffraction, spectroscopic techniques or the properties of molecules in solution. The discussion of the application of physical techniques has been limited to the area of protein synthesis and the related problem of virus structure. This reflects the enormous interest which these problems have excited in the last twenty years, although of course it must be remembered that important advances have also been made in many other fields, for example muscular contraction, photosynthesis and nervous conduction. In another twenty or even five or ten years, an article such as this might be expected to concentrate much more on the role of membranes in biological systems, on development as studied in embryology and morphogenesis and certainly on the structure and function of the nervous system and brain itself. The discussions in §§4, 5 and 6 have emphasized the deterministic quality of biological function in reproduction and growth. The concept of a vital force has given way to a description of biological phenomena in terms of molecular structures and interactions obeying physical laws. The next few years should show whether a similar determinism can be formulated to describe the function of the brain.

Acknowledgments

I am grateful to Professor Sir John Randall, for provision of facilities and encouragement, to Professor M. H. F. Wilkins, Dr. S. Arnott, Dr. M. Spencer, Dr. J. Venable, W. Pigram and D. Dover for discussion, Miss A. Kernaghan and Miss C. Ward for help with preparation of the manuscript and Mr. Z. Gabor for photographic work.

References

Arndt, U. W., and Phillips, D. C., 1961, *Acta Cryst.*, **14**, 807.
Arnott, S., *et al.*, 1966, *Nature, Lond.*, **211**, 227.
Arnott, S., and Wonacott, A. J., 1966 a, *Polymer*, **7**, 157.
—— 1966 b, *J. Molec. Biol.*, **21**, 371.
Bamford, C. H., Elliott, A., and Hanby, W. E., 1956, *Synthetic Polypeptides* (New York: Academic Press).
Blake, C. C. F., *et al.*, 1965, *Nature, Lond.*, **206**, 757.
Bodo, G., Dintzis, H. M., Kendrew, J. C., and Wyckoff, H. W., 1959, *Proc. Roy. Soc.* A, **253**, 70.
Bokhoven, C., Schoone, J. C., and Bijvoet, J. M., 1951, *Acta Cryst.*, **4**, 275.
Bradbury, E. M., *et al.*, 1962, *J. Molec. Biol.*, **5**, 230.
Brant, D. A., and Flory, P. J., 1965, *J. Amer. Chem. Soc.*, **87**, 2788.
Braunitzer, G., Hilse, K., Rudolf, V., and Hilschmann, N., 1964, *Advanc. Protein Chem.*, **19**, 1.
Caspar, D. L. D., 1966, *J. Molec. Biol.*, **15**, 365.
Caspar, D. L. D., and Klug, A., 1962, *Cold Spr. Harb. Symp. Quant. Biol.*, **27**, 1.
Cooper, P. J., and Hamilton, L. D., 1966, *J. Molec. Biol.*, **16**, 562.
Cowan, P. M., McGavin, S., and North, A. C. T., 1955, *Nature, Lond.*, **176**, 1062.
Crick, F. H. C., 1966, *J. Molec. Biol.*, **19**, 548.
Crick, F. H. C., and Watson, J. D., 1956, *Nature, Lond.*, **177**, 473.
Cullis, A. F., *et al.*, 1961, *Proc. Roy. Soc.* A, **265**, 15.
—— 1962, *Proc. Roy. Soc.* A, **265**, 161.

De Santis, P., Giglio, E., Liquori, A. M., and Ripamonti, A., 1962, *Nuovo Cim.*, **26**, 616.
—— 1963, *J. Polymer Sci.*, **A1**, 1383.
—— 1965, *Nature, Lond.*, **206**, 456.
DeVoe, H., and Tinoco, I., Jr., 1962, *J. Molec. Biol.*, **4**, 500.
Diamond, R., 1966, *Acta Cryst.*, **21**, 253.
Dickerson, R. E., 1964, *The Proteins*, Vol. II (New York, London: Academic Press).
Donohue, J., 1952, *J. Phys. Chem.*, **56**, 502.
Edmundson, A. B., 1965, *Nature, Lond.*, **205**, 883.
Elliott, A., 1965, *J. Sci. Instrum.*, **42**, 312.
Feigin, L. A., and Dembo, A. T., 1967, *Acta Cryst.*, in the press.
Finch, J. T., and Klug, A., 1966, *J. Molec. Biol.*, **15**, 344.
Franklin, R. E., and Gosling, R. G., 1953 a, *Nature, Lond.*, **171**, 740.
—— 1953 b, *Acta Cryst.*, **6**, 673.
Fuller, W., 1959, *J. Phys. Chem.*, **63**, 1705.
Fuller, W., and Waring, M., 1963, *Bunsenges. phys. Chem.*, **68**, 805.
Fuller, W., Wilkins, M. H. F., Wilson, H. R., and Hamilton, L. D., 1965, *J. Molec. Biol.*, **12**, 60.
Hamilton, L. D., Fuller, W., and Reich, E., 1963, *Nature, Lond.*, **198**, 538.
Holley, R. W., *et al.*, 1965, *Science*, **147**, 1462.
Huggins, M. L., 1943, *Chem. Rev.*, **32**, 195.
—— 1952, *J. Amer. Chem. Soc.*, **74**, 3963.
Jacob, F., and Monod, J., 1961, *J. Molec. Biol.*, **3**, 318.
Johnson, L. N., and Phillips, D. C., 1965, *Nature, Lond.*, **206**, 761.
Kauzmann, W., 1959, *Advanc. Protein Chem.*, **14**, 1.
Kellenberger, E., 1966 a, *Ciba Foundation Symp.*, *Principles of Biomolecular Organization*, (London: Churchill), p. 192.
—— 1966 b, *Sci. Amer.*, **215**, 32.
Kendrew, J. C., 1964, *Nobel Lectures in Chemistry*, 1942–1962 (Amsterdam: Elsevier).
Kendrew, J. C., *et al.*, 1960, *Nature, Lond.*, **185**, 422.
Kitaigarodski, A. I., 1961, *Organic Chemical Crystallography* (New York: Heywood).
Klug, A., and Berger, J. E., 1964, *J. Molec. Biol.*, **10**, 565.
Klug, A., and Caspar, D. L. D., 1960, *Advanc. Virus Res.*, **7**, 225.
Klug, A., and De Rosier, D. J., 1966, *Nature, Lond.*, **212**, 29.
Klug, A., Finch, J. T., Leberman, R., and Longley, W., 1966, *Ciba Foundation Symp.*, *Principles of Biomolecular Organization* (London: Churchill), p. 158.
Langridge, R., and Gomatos, P. J., 1963, *Science*, **141**, 694.
Langridge, R., *et al.*, 1960, *J. Molec. Biol.*, **2**, 38.
Leach, S. J., Némethy, G., and Scheraga, H. A., 1966, *Biopolymers*, **4**, 369.
Lerman, L. S., 1961, *J. Molec. Biol.*, **3**, 18.
Levinthal, C., 1966, *Sci. Amer.*, **214**, 42.
Lipscomb, W. N., *et al.*, 1966, *J. Molec. Biol.*, **19**, 423.
Liquori, A. M., 1966, *Ciba Foundation Symp.*, *Principles of Biomolecular Organization* (London: Churchill), p. 40.
Liquori, A., De Santis, P., Kovacs, A. L., and Mazzarella, L., 1966, *Nature, Lond.*, **211**, 1039.
McElroy, W. D., and Glass, B. (Eds), 1957, *The Chemical Basis of Heredity* (Baltimore: Johns Hopkins Press).
Madison, J. T., Everett, G. A., and Kung, H., 1966, *Science*, **153**, 531.
Markham, R., Frey, S., and Hills, G. J., 1963, *Virology*, **20**, 88.
Markham, R., Hitchborn, J. H., Hills, G. J., and Frey, S., 1964, *Virology*, **22**, 342.
Marmur, J., and Doty, P., 1959, *Nature, Lond.*, **183**, 1427.
Marvin, D. A., Wilkins, M. H. F., and Hamilton, L. D., 1966, *Acta Cryst.*, **20**, 663.
Monod, J., Changeux, J., and Jacob, F., 1963, *J. Molec. Biol.*, **6**, 306.
Monod, J., Wyman, J., and Changeux, J. P., 1965, *J. Molec. Biol.*, **12**, 88.
Muirhead, H., and Perutz, M. F., 1963, *Nature, Lond.*, **199**, 633.
North, A. C. T., 1965, *Acta Cryst.*, **18**, 212.

Parry, D. A. D., and Elliott, A., 1965, *Nature, Lond.*, **206**, 616.
Pauling, L., 1960, *The Nature of the Chemical Bond*, 3rd edn (Ithaca, N.Y.: Cornell University Press).
Pauling, L., and Corey, R. B., 1951, *Proc. Nat. Acad. Sci., Wash.*, **37**, 729.
Pauling, L., Corey, R. B., and Bransom, H. R., 1951, *Proc. Nat. Acad. Sci., Wash.*, **37**, 205.
Perutz, M. F., 1963, *Science*, **140**, 863.
—— 1965, *J. Molec. Biol.*, **13**, 646.
Perutz, M. F., *et al.*, 1964, *Nature, Lond.*, **203**, 687.
Perutz, M. F., Kendrew, J. C., and Watson, H. C., 1965, *J. Molec. Biol.*, **13**, 669.
Ramachandran, G. N., and Kartha, G., 1954, *Nature, Lond.*, **174**, 369.
Ramachandran, G. N., and Raman, S., 1956, *Curr. Sci.*, **25**, 348.
Ramakrishnan, C., and Ramachandran, G. N., 1965, *Biophys. J.*, **5**, 909.
Rich, A., and Crick, F. H. C., 1955, *Nature, Lond.*, **176**, 915.
—— 1961, *J. Molec. Biol.*, **3**, 483.
Sato, T., *et al.*, 1966, *J. Molec. Biol.*, **16**, 180.
Scheraga, H. A., Leach, S. J., Scott, R. A., and Némethy, G., 1965, *Disc. Faraday Soc.*, **40**, 268.
Scott, R. A., and Scheraga, H. A., 1966, *J. Chem. Phys.*, **44**, 3054.
Scouloudi, H., 1960, *Proc. Roy. Soc.* A, **258**, 181.
Smith, D. B., 1964, *J. Amer. Chem. Soc.*, **84**, 4240.
Spencer, M., 1959, *Acta Cryst.*, **12**, 66.
Spencer, M., Fuller, W., Wilkins, M. H. F., and Brown, G. L., 1962, *Nature, Lond.*, **194**, 1014.
Spencer, M., and Poole, F., 1965, *J. Molec. Biol.*, **11**, 314.
Taylor, C. A., Hinde, R. M., and Lipson, H., 1951, *Acta Cryst.*, **4**, 261.
Tomita, K. I., and Rich, A., 1964, *Nature, Lond.*, **201**, 1160.
Trumanyan, V. G., Esipova, N. G., and Kisselev, L., 1967, *Acta Cryst.*, in the press.
Vanderkooi, G., *et al.*, 1966, *Biochemistry*, **5**, 2991.
Watson, J. D., and Crick, F. H. C., 1953 a, *Nature, Lond.*, **171**, 964.
—— 1953 b, *Nature, Lond.*, **171**, 737.
Wilkins, M. H. F., 1963, *Science*, **140**, 941.
Wilkins, M. H. F., Stokes, A. R., and Wilson, H. R., 1953, *Nature, Lond.*, **171**, 738.
Zachau, H. G., Dütting, D., and Feldmann, H., 1966, *Angew. Chem.*, **78**, 392.

PHYSICAL CONTRIBUTIONS TO THE DETERMINATION OF BIOLOGICAL STRUCTURE AND FUNCTION

W. Fuller

ADDENDUM

De Rosier and Klug (1968) have described a method of calculating three-dimensional images of structures seen in electron micrographs by a method analogous to the Fourier synthesis technique of X-ray crystal structure analysis. Methods of revealing periodicities in electron micrographs have been described (Elliott, Lowy, and Squire 1968; Fiskin and Beer 1968) in which a simple optical arrangement is used to generate the self-convolution of the electron micrograph. By analogy with the Patterson function of X-ray crystallography, where peaks correspond to interatomic separations in the original structure, the principal peaks in this function correspond to the principal structural periodicities in the original micrograph. Hookes *et al.* (1968) have described a computer procedure for calculating the expected electron microscope image for a tubular structure as a function of its orientation, its stain distribution, and any distortion of the tubule from a circular to elliptical cross section.

The development of a system in which an automatic microdensitometer is linked to a computer (unpublished work of U. W. Arndt, R. A. Crowther, and J. F. W. Mallett) allows an X-ray diffraction pattern to be scanned and the optical density sampled at regular points on a grid. It is likely that this method of determining X-ray diffraction intensities will be much used in protein crystal structure analysis at the expense of automatic diffractometers where ionization counters are used. An elegant technique of particular use in determining intensities in X-ray fibre diffraction patterns has been developed by Elliott (see Elliott *et al.* 1968). A modified Michelson interferometer is used to produce a fringe pattern which corresponds to contours of optical density.

This method is particularly useful since it allows the apparent position of a diffraction spot to be corrected for the effect of varying intensity in the background.

The crystallization of a transfer RNA species (Clark _et al._ 1968) is an important advance in structural studies of this biologically important molecule, since the mere fact of crystallization supports the idea that the molecule has a well-defined rather than a 'floppy' structure. So far only microcrystalline preparations have been reported, but even these may be adequate for a preliminary structure analysis if used in conjunction with the nucleotide sequence of the RNA and molecular model building techniques. Such model building studies have already been used to derive a model for the region of the transfer RNA containing the anticodon (Fuller and Hodgson 1967). An X-ray analysis of synthetic RNA double helices (Arnott _et al._ 1968) has allowed the geometry of the RNA helix to be more closely defined than was possible by studies on natural RNA's. Further, it has led to the discovery of a structural transition for the RNA helix from a helix with 11 to one with 12 nucleotide pairs per helix pitch. These studies also showed that, in contrast to what was previously thought, these synthetic RNA's assume structures completely analogous to those of the natural occurring RNA's.

A great deal or work is in progress on the structural analysis of crystalline proteins. Because of its great biological importance and the difficulties which the problem presented, thc analysis of ribonuclease at close to atomic resolution (Avey _et al._ 1967, Kartha _et al._ 1967, Wyckoff _et al._ 1967) is particularly interesting. By solving the structure with molecules which inhibit the enzyme's function bound to its active site, it is possible to obtain information on the way the enzyme functions. The analysis of reduced and oxy-haemoglobin is important for a number of reasons. First, the analysis has now reached the stage where many diseases arising from abnormal haemoglobins can be understood in stereochemical terms (Perutz and Lehmann 1968). Secondly, since haemoglobin consists of four subunits whose interactions are related to the binding of oxygen by a haem group in each subunit, this study (Perutz _et al._ 1968) provides a great deal of information on specific interactions between protein molecules. Such information may be useful in studies on structures built up from protein subunits (e.g. viruses, bacterial flagella) as well as in those on other oligomeric enzymes. Thirdly, analysis of the known amino-acid sequences for the large number of haemoglobins which have similar tertiary structure should contribute to our understanding of the factors which define protein chain folding. Information on this is also being provided by X-ray studies of other protein crystal structures, e.g. chymotrypsin (Sigler et al. 1968).

Ordered arrays of ribosomes have recently been seen in the electron microscope (Morgan and Uzman 1966, Byers 1967). The helical and tetragonal symmetry of these arrangements might be expected to reflect some internal symmetry in the ribosome itself (Morgan and Kellogg 1967). Although no detailed information about ribosomal structure has so far been obtained from these studies they will encourage efforts to obtain crystalline arrays of ribosomes which are of sufficient size for X-ray diffraction analysis. After many years of investigation by electron microscopy and X-ray diffraction.

evidence for ordered structure in chromosomes is being obtained. It appears that the basic structural unit may be a threadlike structure with a diameter of approximately 170 Å and probably a central hole. At the nuclear membrane these threads tend to orient themselves with a centre-to-centre separation of approximately 280 Å (Davies 1968, Davies and Small 1968). It is possible that these 'unit threads' may correspond to the super coiled model for nucleohistone proposed by Pardon *et al.* (1967).

The work reviewed in this Addendum adds further support to the conclusions drawn in the original article. In particular, these studies highlight still further the high degree of order and symmetry in biological structures and the fact that biological macromolecules can be expected to have well-defined rather than 'floppy' structures.

REFERENCES

Arnott, S., Fuller, W., Hodgson, A., and Prutton, I., 1968, *Nature, Lond.*, **220**, 561.

Avey, H. P., Boles, M. O., Carlisle, C. H., *et al.*, 1967, *Nature, Lond.*, **213**, 557.

Byers, B., 1967, *J. Molec. Biol.*, **26**, 155.

Clark, B. F. C., Doctor, B. P., Holmes, K. C., *et al.*, 1968, *Nature, Lond.*, **219**, 1222.

Davies, H. G., 1968, *J. Cell Sci.*, **3**, 124.

Davies, H. G., and Small, J. V., 1968, *Nature, Lond.*, **217**, 1122.

De Rosier, D. J., and Klug, A., 1968, *Nature, Lond.*, **217**, 130.

Elliott, A., Lowy, J., Parry, D. A. D., and Vibert, P. J., 1968, *Nature, Lond.*, **218**, 656.

Elliott, A., Lowy, J., and Squire, J. M., 1968, *Nature, Lond.*, **219**, 1224.

Fiskin, A. M., and Beer, M., 1968, *Science*, **159**, 1111.

Fuller, W., and Hodgson, A., 1967, *Nature, Lond.*, **215**, 817.

Hookes, D. E., Randall, Sir John, and Hopkins, J. M., 1968, *Symp. Int. Soc. Cell Biol.*, Vol. 6, p. 115.

Kartha, G., Bello, J., and Harker, D., 1967, *Nature, Lond.*, **213**, 862.

Morgan, R. S., and Kellogg, F. D., 1967, _Nature, Lond._, **216**, 1302.

Morgan, R. S., and Uzman, B. G., 1966, _Science_, **152**, 214.

Pardon, J. F., Wilkins, M. H. F., and Richards, B. M., 1967, _Nature, Lond._, **215**, 508.

Perutz, M. F., and Lehmann, H., 1968, _Nature, Lond._, **219**, 902.

Perutz, M. F., Muirhead, H., Cox, J. M., and Goaman, L. C. G., 1968, _Nature, Lond._, **219**, 131.

Sigler, P. B., Blow, D. M., Matthews, B. W., and Henderson, R., 1968, _J. Molec. Biol._, **35**, 143.

Wyckoff, H. W., Hardman, K. D., Allewell, N. M., _et al._, 1967, _J. Biol. Chem._, **242**, 3984.

W. Fuller
November 1968

Sense organs—transducers of the environment

C. RASHBASS

Institute of Psychiatry, The Maudsley Hospital, University of London

Contents

Abstract. Most animals have a central nervous system. Sense organs are the structures that convert information about the outside world and the inside environment into a form suitable for processing by the central nervous system. The most usual form into which this information is transformed is a series of propagated nerve impulses. A nerve impulse is a self-propagating conductance change in a nerve membrane. It is initiated by an electric current being driven outwards through the membrane, and some sense organs are known to generate such currents. Sensory cells are stimulated only by mechanical deformation, light, temperature change or certain chemicals. Sense organs consist of appropriate sensory cells and subsidiary physical structures that present aspects of the environment in the form of a stimulus. The magnitude of the output of sense organs is non-linearly related to the input. Frequently the output is approximately proportional to the logarithm of the input. Most sense organs have band-pass frequency characteristics: emphasis is given to the rate of change of the input but short stimuli are transformed ballistically. The eye and skin show spatial characteristics analogous to these temporal ones: rate of change with respect to position is emphasized, and summation over small areas takes place. Spatial and temporal properties interact. Colour discrimination by the eye has only three degrees of freedom. Recent observations have confirmed that there are three types of cone in the eye, each containing its own photolabile pigment. Receptor cells generate noise and in certain circumstances the eye behaves as a judge of constant fallibility in identifying signals in the presence of noise. Some sense organs are under control of the central nervous system, either as a relay of feedback information or in an independent manner.

1. Introduction

All animals, except the very simplest, have a nervous system. The main function of this system is to control much of their internal economy and almost all of their external relations. To perform this function the nervous system needs to receive information about the state of the animal's environment, both external and internal. Within the nervous system this information is processed in a variety of ways: it is transported, transformed, analysed, interacted and stored. During these operations the information may be represented in any of several different forms: transport of information from one place in the nervous system to another is achieved by means of electrical disturbances travelling along the surface of nerve fibres; transformation, analysis and interaction of information take place at the nerve cells, or in regions close to nerve cells. Here the information may be represented by the state of the electrical properties of the membrane enveloping the cell, or by the presence of one of a small number of chemical substances that can be emitted by nerve cells and that are capable of changing the electrical properties of neighbouring cells. In whatever form the information may be, that form is independent of the content of the message; a nerve impulse travelling along a fibre in the nerve from the eye to the brain is not different in any important way from an impulse bringing information from the ear to the brain. In general, the intensity of a signal is represented by the frequency of impulses being transmitted and the content of a signal depends on which fibres are carrying the impulses. Further information about the nature of the stimulus may be contained in the relative frequencies of impulses in many associated fibres—the overall pattern of impulses.

To obtain information concerning the environment the nervous system needs to be associated with a variety of structures that are able to detect, and frequently able to measure, some quality of the environment and to translate this information into a form suitable to the nervous system. These structures are the sense organs.

The range of qualities detected by the sense organs is very wide. In man, in addition to the classical five senses, there are organs sensitive to pain, heat and cold, vibration, the direction of gravitational forces, and linear and rotational accelerations. There is an even greater variety of organs concerned with the detection and monitoring of processes going on within the body. Body temperature, blood sugar concentration, blood pressure and osmolarity are but a few of these. There are specialized organs concerned with the position of limbs and the contraction of muscles. Some of the detectors of the internal state are situated in parts of the body concerned with the quality that they detect, but many, particularly those concerned with maintaining the chemical composition of the body stable, are specialized cells buried deeply within the brain.

The sense organ may be looked upon as a system that has an input and an output. The input is the environmental property being detected. The output is usually a pattern of nerve impulses travelling along a number of nerve fibres to the central nervous system. It is possible that the receptor cells within the structure of the brain, about which little is known, interact with other cells in their immediate neighbourhood. In this case the sensory information may not be represented in the form of nerve impulses and the output of such a sensory system could reasonably be considered to be the electrical state of the cell membrane.

By way of introduction we can briefly outline the chain of events between the input and the output of sense organs. The output is almost invariably a train of nerve impulses. There is evidence from some types of receptor that these impulses are preceded by a change in the potential across the membrane of the receptor cell and this is probably true of all receptors. Receptor potentials are produced in cells by one of a small number of types of change. Mechanical deformation, light, temperature changes or the presence of a particular chemical substance are probably the only ways to evoke generator potentials in human sensory organs. Some fish have specialized sensory structures that are remarkably sensitive to the passage of an electric current (Murray 1965, Mullinger 1964) and it is possible that it is their function to detect small electric currents in the sea. In the whole of the animal kingdom there may exist cells responding directly to other stimuli, but the four types listed above are overwhelmingly the most common. We can call the process, whereby one of these basic stimuli causes the sensory cell to develop a generator potential, the primary transducer action. This is the link in the chain of events of sensory detection about which least is known.

The central nervous system is informed about a wide variety of different aspects of the environment. The sense of vision detects not only the presence or absence of light but also its intensity and colour, and its spatial and temporal distribution. The sense of hearing analyses sound into qualities of pitch and intensity, and position of the source. The basic stimuli to which sensory cells can respond are limited to the few mentioned above, and so the sensory cells are frequently associated with subsidiary structures that transform the environmental qualities into a form that allows their detection by the sensory cells. In many cases the sense organ distorts the information that it transmits to the central nervous system by the introduction of non-linearity into the transformation, or by the non-uniformity of its frequency characteristics, in such a way as to emphasize events that are of particular biological significance to the animal.

There are occasions when we find that the performance of a sense organ is dependent on its own output. This dependence involves a process of feedback of information to the sense organ. The feedback path is sometimes situated locally within the sense organ, and sometimes involves transmission into the central nervous system and back out from there to the sense organ. There is also evidence that sense organs may sometimes function in a way that is dependent on activity going on within the central nervous system.

We shall now consider the processes involved in sensory detection in greater detail.

2. The generation of nerve impulses

Our knowledge of the nature of the nerve impulse, the process by which it is initiated and the method whereby it is transmitted owes much to the work of

Hodgkin and Huxley (1952) on the giant nerve fibre of the squid. This has been reviewed by Hodgkin (1958) and has been the subject of one of these articles (Fatt 1958).

The nerve fibre is essentially a tubular membrane separating two solutions of different chemical composition. Inside the membrane is the axoplasm in which the concentration of potassium is high and the concentration of sodium is low. The fibre is bathed on the outside by the extracellular fluid in which the concentration of sodium is high and of potassium low. It had been known for a long time that, when the nerve is not stimulated, there is a difference of potential across the membrane, the outside being some 60 mv positive to the inside.

The basic type of experiment that Hodgkin performed was to insert fine electrodes up the inside of the giant squid fibre. He imposed a sudden change of potential across the membrane and then, by means of a feedback amplifier, maintained the potential at that level. With the voltage across the membrane clamped in this way he measured the time course of the current across the membrane. This type of experiment was carried out with different concentrations of sodium in the external fluid. In this way he was able to talk of changes occurring in the sodium conductance and the potassium conductance brought about by imposed changes in the membrane potential.

At rest the potassium conductance was found to be small but, even so, much greater than sodium conductance. The membrane potential at rest is fairly close to the equilibrium potential of the potassium ion. If the potential across the membrane is clamped at a lower level there is a transient change in the sodium conductance, which rapidly rises and then slowly decays to its original level. The effect on the potassium conductance is a delayed and sustained rise occurring roughly coincidently with the decay in sodium conductance. From these data Hodgkin and Huxley were able to compute the course of events that would follow a brief imposition of a reduction of membrane voltage that is not clamped but allowed to act under its own potential changes. At first the sodium conductance rises and sodium ions enter the fibre. This inward current makes the inside of the fibre positive with respect to the outside. At the crest of this potential change the slow changes due to the initial reduction of potential begin to take effect. Sodium conductance declines and potassium conductance rises so that potassium ions leave the fibre faster than sodium ions enter it. As a result the potential swings back towards the equilibrium potential of the potassium ion. These slow effects persist after the end of the potential swing and render the fibre relatively insensitive to the effects of a further induced potential change.

This sequence of events constitutes the action potential of a nerve impulse. It results in a little sodium being gained by the inside of the fibre and a little potassium being lost from it. These are slowly restored to their original site by a process, known as sodium pumping, that draws the energy required to move the ions against the concentration gradient from metabolic activity.

The inrush of sodium ions into the fibre at the peak of the action potential draws sodium ions away from the tissue fluid bathing the nearby inactive membrane. This reduces the potential across the neighbouring inactive membrane and starts a cycle of activity there, in this way propagating the nerve impulse along the whole length of the fibre.

The general principles of excitation and conduction of the nerve impulse in the giant fibre of the squid apply to many other excitable tissues including the nerves of vertebrate animals and various types of muscle fibre. There are variations in the magnitudes of the parameters, and the time constants of the process depend on the tissue. In many vertebrate nerve fibres there is a structural difference that we need to consider. These fibres are enveloped by a sheath of a fatty material that is virtually impermeable to the passage of ions. This sheath, the myelin sheath, is absent at small regions distributed along the length of the fibre. These regions are known as the nodes of Ranvier. When the membrane at one node of Ranvier is active and sodium current is passing through it, the return path of the current is extended along the nerve fibre by the insulating myelin to pass through the membrane at the next few nodes. The next node carries most of this current and its

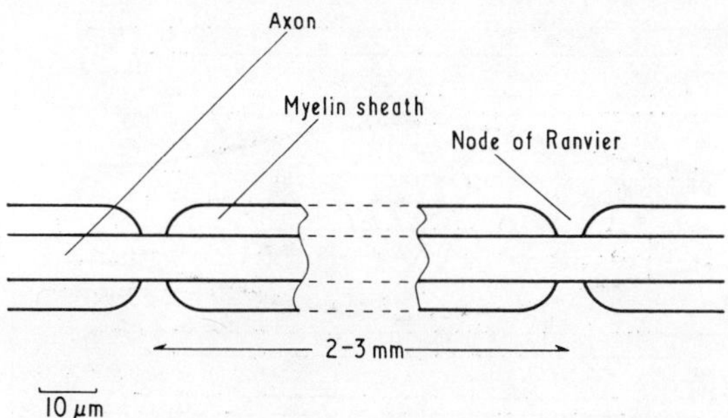

Figure 1. A medullated nerve fibre. This, and all subsequent illustrations, are diagrammatic and the scales approximate.

resting potential is reduced first until the membrane there is triggered into activity. Excitation in effect jumps from node to node and increase in the velocity of propagation results (Huxley and Stämpfli 1949).

We have seen that the propagation of impulses along a nerve fibre is brought about by the lowering of the resting potential across the membrane. It might be expected that sensory cells, when stimulated, produce potential changes that do this. Such potential changes have been demonstrated in several sense organs and have been variously called receptor potentials or generator potentials.

3. The receptor potential

Potential changes developed by the stimulation of a sensory cell were demonstrated by Katz (1950 a, b) in muscle spindles. Muscle spindles are specialized structures found in the skeletal muscles of vertebrate animals. (Skeletal muscles are those concerned with movement of the body and limbs, and are distinguished from the muscles of the heart and other internal organs.) Vertebrate skeletal muscles are composed of numerous long cylindrical structures, which when suitably stained or illuminated show an appearance of cross striation. These are the muscle fibres. Buried among the muscle fibres are small groups of one to twelve fibres that differ in appearance from the rest. In the middle of their length they show no cross striations and in this non-striated region the small group of muscle fibres is enclosed in a spindle-shaped membrane. These modified muscle fibres are known as intrafusal fibres. There are two types of sensory nerve fibres emerging from the spindle. There is one large fibre coming from nerve endings that spiral around the muscle fibres in the spindle. This is the annulo-spiral or primary ending. There may also be one or two finer sensory nerve fibres coming from 'flower spray' or secondary endings. The intrafusal muscle fibres have their own motor nerve fibres and shorten in response to impulses arriving along these nerve fibres. It had long been known (Adrian 1926, Matthews 1931) that muscle spindles were sensory organs

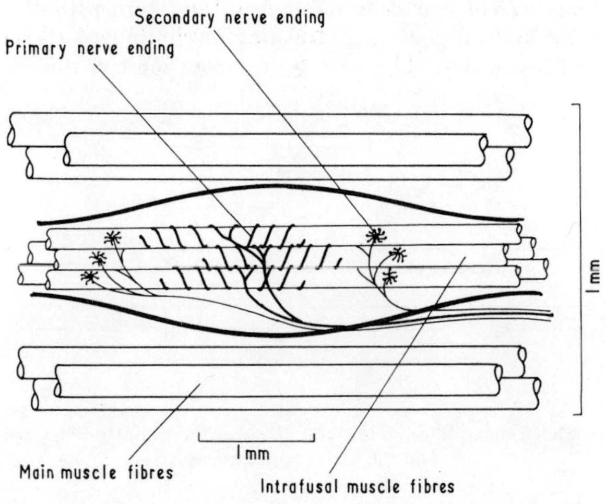

Figure 2. A muscle spindle. The difference in the longitudinal and transverse scales should be noted.

responding to passive stretching of the muscle by initiating a train of impulse in their sensory nerve fibres. Katz (1950 a, b) placed a recording electrode on a primary sensory fibre as it emerged from the muscle spindle and examined the potential changes that occurred when the muscle was stretched. He found that many muscle spindles generated a low frequency of action potentials that were propagated down the fibre even when the spindle was not being stretched. He also detected small action potentials that were not propagated down the fibre. These discrete local action potentials could also be discerned at the beginning of the propagated action potentials. The small non-propagated abortive active potentials could be seen to follow one another with intervals as small as 1 msec, but following a propagated action potential all activity, propagated or abortive, was absent for some 50 msec. The abortive action potentials were not all the same size. However, in any one preparation their sizes could take values chosen from a small number of possibilities. Katz suggested that these abortive action potentials were evidence of activity in individual branches of the sensory fibre and that propagation only occurred when there was coincidence in the activity of more than one branch. Propagated activity would spread into all the branches and make them refractory, thus explaining the inactivity following a propagated action potential. He also suggested that the random intervals at which the abortive action potentials occurred might be explicable either in terms of molecular agitation in the mechanical receptor substance or in terms of ionic noise in the receptor membrane.

When the muscle containing the muscle spindle was stretched, the frequency of propagated action potentials was increased and the number of abortive action potentials reduced. The records of these propagated action potentials obtained by an electrode placed near the muscle spindle showed that the action potentials were accompanied by a shift in the baseline level of potential in a negative direction. This potential change developed with the first action potential and was sustained during the course of the mechanical stretch. When a local anaesthetic was applied

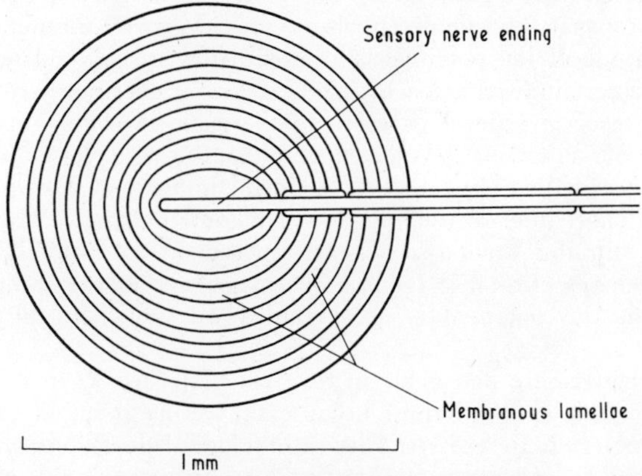

Figure 3. A Pacinian corpuscle.

to the preparation, the action potentials were abolished but the sustained potential drop during stretch was retained. The magnitude of this generator potential increased with the magnitude of the stretch, and was much more intense during periods in which the stretch was being increased. Katz talks of two effects: the static effect and the more intense dynamic effect. The relationship of the potential change to the extension of the muscle in the case of the static effect, and the rate of extension in the case of the dynamic effect, is monotonic but non-linear. In both cases the effects are relatively greater at low levels of stretch and slow stretching than they are at high levels of stretch and rapid stretching. On the other hand, the relationship between the frequency of transmitted impulses and the magnitude of the generator potential was rather close to being linear.

On relaxation of the muscle after a period of being stretched the generator potential changed transiently to a value more positive than the resting level. During this phase there was a lower frequency of propagated action potentials than the resting frequency.

Another sense organ in which a receptor potential has been demonstrated is the Pacinian corpuscle. This is a structure that is found widely distributed under the skin and around the internal organs of many vertebrate animals. Structurally it consists of a series of concentric membranes surrounding the non-medullated end of a medullated nerve fibre. The corpuscle is quite large, being about 1 mm long and about 0·5 mm in transverse diameter, and frequently engulfs the first node of Ranvier of the emerging nerve fibre. It is known to be sensitive to deformation.

The generator potential has been recorded by placing an electrode on the nerve as it emerges from the corpuscle (Alvarez-Buylla and de Arellano 1953, Gray and Sato 1953) and stimulating the receptor by the movement of an electromechanical transducer. Unlike the muscle spindle the Pacinian corpuscle is not spontaneously active. When compressed it emits only a short train of impulses even if the compression is maintained. On relaxing compression there is a further burst of action potentials. The generator potential can be discerned in the records of the action potentials obtained from a point on the nerve near the corpuscle. Local anaesthetic abolishes the propagated action potentials leaving the generator potential unaffected.

The magnitude of the potential is approximately linearly related to the compression until a certain level is reached above which it does not rise. The potential decays in 3–5 msec and develops again in the same direction on the release of pressure. There is a marked dynamic effect in that during a phase of rising pressure the potential exceeds that obtained by sustained stimulation. Two pressure stimuli separated by a short interval each produce a potential change. The potential due to the second stimulus can be seen superimposed on the first. However, as the interval between the stimuli is reduced the magnitude of the second diminishes, illustrating that the potential is accompanied by some sort of depression or refractoriness.

Potential changes are detectable in the vertebrate eye when it is illuminated. These are not simple to interpret because the retina is an atypically complex structure. The vertebrate eye starts its embryological development as part of the brain from which it separates, reaching its final position outside the skull. It is connected to the brain by a large number of nerve fibres, which are collected together into a bundle called the optic nerve. The optic nerve bears only a superficial resemblance to other sensory nerves as it is really a tract of fibres joining the brain to a complex of nerve cells that have remained associated with the light-sensitive cells on the outside of the skull. The optic nerve shows certain structural differences from peripheral nerve trunks, and in the mammal shares with the nerve tracts within the brain the inability to regenerate after being cut. The retina, which is the whole of the excitable and nervous layer at the back of the eye, contains many structures that in other sensory systems would be found in the brain. The receptor cells, which in man and some other animals can be recognized under the microscope as being of two types, the rods and the cones, form the outermost layer of the retina. Lying in front (in the path of the light) of the light-sensitive parts of the rods and cones are the main bodies of these cells, and several layers of other cells, some with short extensions passing backwards and forwards through the thickness of the retina (the bipolar cells), some with processes ramifying in the plane of the retina (the horizontal cells) and some with more complex configurations. In front of all these lie the large bodies of the ganglion cells, from which medullated fibres arise that are gathered together to pass through the retina and out at the back of the eye to form the optic nerve. It has long been known that slow potential changes can be recorded from the eyes when they are illuminated. These potential changes are known as the electroretinogram. The retina can be removed from the frog's eye and still shows electrical responses to illumination similar to those obtained from the intact eye, and it is generally agreed that the electroretinogram originates in the retina. Experiments with microelectrodes placed at different depths in the retina (Tomita 1950, Ottoson and Svaetichin 1953, Brindley 1956) suggest that most of the electrical activity detected in the electroretinogram is generated by the bipolar cells. Electrical activity recorded from a microelectrode placed close to the outer surface of the rods and cones (Ottoson and Svaetichin 1952) does not convincingly originate in these cells (for a full discussion of this problem, see Brindley 1960, chap. 2).

Microelectrodes inserted into the retinae of some fish show electrical changes that are closely related to illumination. They come on when the light is switched on and remain until the light is switched off. The magnitude of the potential change is dependent on intensity and on wavelength (Svaetichin 1953, MacNichol and Svaetichin 1958, Svaetichin and MacNichol 1958). Svaetichin originally thought these to be potentials evoked in the cones, but the evidence from the position of the electrode tip suggests that they arise nearer the front of the retina in the region of bipolar and horizontal cells.

The compound eyes of invertebrates are relatively simple, consisting of units or ommatidia, each of which has a small number of light-sensitive cells. Each light-sensitive cell has its own nerve fibre. Many of these have been studied, that of the king crab (*Limulus*) extensively (Hartline *et al.* 1952). A microelectrode inserted into the light-sensitive cell of *Limulus* shows that when the cell is illuminated a potential change occurs across the cell membrane. The potential change does not begin until 100–500 msec after the cell is lit. The magnitude of the beginning of the change is linearly related to the intensity of the light, but the steady-state value is roughly proportional to the logarithm of the intensity (Fuortes and Hodgkin 1964). Action potentials are propagated along the nerve fibres from the light-sensitive cells and the frequency of these impulses is linearly related to the magnitude of the potential change. The magnitude of the receptor potential evoked by a brief flash is related to the current level of illumination and to the immediate past history of the illumination of the receptor. These properties resemble the effect of past and current illumination on the sensitivity of the human eye and will be discussed later.

4. The primary transducer action

The sequence of events whereby some simple physical or chemical change in a receptor cell results in a change of potential across its membrane is the core of the biological transducer mechanism, and it is about this sequence of events that least is known.

4.1. *Mechanically sensitive receptors*

Potential changes that occur across the membranes of nerve fibres are caused primarily by a change in the conductance of the membrane to sodium ions. Replacement of the fluid bathing the outside of the fibre by a solution containing no sodium results in the abolition of all activity. Early experiments on receptor potentials generated by mechanically sensitive cells (Katz 1950 b, Gray and Sato 1953) suggested that sodium deprivation only blocks the propagated action potentials arising in the sensory nerve fibres, leaving the receptor potential unaffected. However, Diamond *et al.* (1958) showed that the apparent immunity of the Pacinian corpuscle to sodium deprivation was due to retention of sodium in the membranous layers surrounding the nerve ending. By perfusing the corpuscle through its blood supply with a sodium-free solution they showed that the receptor potential was reduced to 10% of its original magnitude in 11–30 min. This effect was reversible, the receptor potential being completely restored by perfusing with a solution containing sodium. The reduction of the receptor potential was graded when solutions of reduced sodium concentrations were used. They conclude that most of the change in the production of the receptor potential is carried by sodium ions. Their inability to abolish completely the receptor potential by sodium deprivation suggests that other ions may contribute to the current.

Similar observations have now been made on the isolated muscle spindle (Ottoson 1964, Calma 1965). Prolonged soaking in a sodium-free solution reduces the receptor potential to 20–30% of its original level. It is never reduced below this level and the effect is reversible. Again it seems that the major part of the current during the receptor potential is carried by sodium ions.

Another approach to this problem is provided by the use of tetrodotoxin, a substance known to block the action potential of nerve and muscle fibres by suppressing the sodium-carrying mechanism (Narahashi *et al.* 1964). Discrepant results are quoted by Loewenstein *et al.* (1963) and Nishi and Sato (1966). In both experiments the effect of tetrodotoxin was investigated on the receptor potential of Pacinian corpuscles from which the lamellae or membranous layers surrounding the non-medullated nerve terminal had been removed by microdissection. The process of stripping the lamellae from the fibre does not reduce its sensitivity to mechanical stimulation. Loewenstein and his co-workers report that tetrodotoxin blocks the propagated impulses selectively without affecting the receptor potential, whereas Nishi and Sato report a reduction in the magnitude of the receptor potential to about 40% of its normal value. It might be possible to reconcile these observations if the removal of the lamellae in the preparations of Loewenstein *et al.* was incomplete. The effect that Nishi and Sato report developed much more slowly than the blocking of the propagated action potentials and it could be that the lamellar remnants are very impermeable to tetrodotoxin.

In this context it is interesting to note that the end-plate potential, a potential change in a specialized structure on skeletal muscle fibres that intermediates between the motor nerve fibre and the muscle fibre, is unaffected by tetrodotoxin (Furukawa *et al.* 1959). The end-plate potential is considered, on other grounds, to result from the non-selective increase in the membrane permeability to all ions (Fatt and Katz 1951). It would appear that the sensory receptor potential is generated differently from the motor end-plate potential although they resemble one another in certain respects.

The way in which deformation of the receptor cell membrane induces selective changes in its ionic permeability is not known. There is reason to believe that the effect of mechanical deformation is limited spatially to the area that is deformed and does not spread beyond that area. Loewenstein and Ishiko (1959) stimulated the sensory terminal of a Pacinian corpuscle, from which the non-nervous surrounding lamellae had been removed, with two electromechanical transducers. Simultaneous stimulation of two sites, or stimulation separated by a short interval, produced a potential change at a nearby recording electrode that was the linear sum of the potentials produced by stimulating those sites individually. Delivering two brief stimuli separated by a short interval to one site did not produce linear summation of the responses—the responses to the second stimulus being greatly reduced. This is the depression or refractoriness of the receptor noted by Gray and Sato (1953).

4.2. *Light-sensitive receptors*

It is probable that excitation of photoreceptive cells by light produces ionic permeability changes in the cell membrane, although these changes have never been convincingly isolated from the other electrical activity going on in the illuminated retina. Some of the processes involved between the falling of light on to the cell and the generation of a hypothetical receptor potential are now understood, but in the main the sequence of events is not known. For incident light to have any effect it needs to be absorbed and this implies the existence of a pigment. Pigments that absorb light of the wavelengths to which the cells are sensitive have been found in many cases. A substance called rhodopsin or visual purple has been extracted from the rods of many vertebrate animals including man. Rhodopsin is a purplish substance that is stable in the dark but bleached by exposure to light. This process is virtually irreversible in aqueous solutions of the pigment but in the living retina regeneration of the purple colour occurs in the dark. The absorption spectrum of rhodopsin closely resembles the spectral sensitivity of the human eye in the fully dark-adapted state and the spectral sensitivity of the eyes of other animals known to contain it. Some fish in whose eyes rhodopsin is absent but which contain another pigment, porphyropsin, show spectral sensitivities that match the absorption spectrum of that pigment. Other pigments have also been found in the rods of other species. The pigments whose presence could be inferred from sensitivity and colour-matching studies in cones have resisted extraction. However, Rushton (1955, 1963 a, b, c, 1965 a, b, c) has demonstrated objectively the existence of two cone pigments in man by retinal densitometry in normal and colour-blind subjects, and Marks (1965) has demonstrated by microspectrophotometry that the cones of goldfish can be divided into three groups, the cells of each group containing an individual pigment.

The chemical identity of the cone pigments has not been established, apart from the possible exception of iodopsin (Wald *et al.* 1955) which can be extracted from the retinae of domestic fowls and has an absorption spectrum comparable with the spectral sensitivity of the light-adapted bird. Our knowledge of the effect of light on the visual pigments is therefore restricted to the rod pigments, rhodopsin in particular.

The rhodopsin molecule is composed of two parts: one part is closely related to retinene, the aldehyde of vitamin A, and the other part, the opsin, is a protein. The action of light is to produce a variety of stereoisomeric changes in the retinene part of the molecule into forms some of which are stable and some unstable. The rhodopsin is found in the outer segments of the rods and is present in high concentration. The rods are dichroic, preferentially absorbing plane-polarized light when the electric vector is perpendicular to their long axis (Denton 1954). Electron microscopy of the outer segments of the rods (de Robertis 1956) shows that they contain a pile of flattened sacs. The walls of the sacs are probably mainly rhodopsin and are not more than ten molecules thick (Brindley 1960, p. 21).

One quantum of light absorbed is sufficient to excite a rod. This statement is based on the measurements of Hecht *et al.* (1942). According to their observations a flash illuminating 500 rods is seen on 60% of occasions when it contains between 54 and 148 quanta arriving at the front of the eye. If we allow for transmission losses through the eye, this suggests an upper limit of 14 quanta absorbed on average by rhodopsin. The probability of one of the 500 rods having absorbed two quanta is 0·178 which is too small to account for seeing 60% of such flashes.

Applying a similar argument to the measurements of Stiles (1939) on the threshold of cones gives an upper limit of 7 to the number of quanta that need to be absorbed within a short time to excite a cone.

The process whereby a light-induced chemical change in a small number of molecules in a cell is able to induce a transmissible electrical change in the cell membrane is not understood.

4.3. *Chemically sensitive receptors*

We have seen that the first change to take place in the detection of light is in the stereoisomerism of a visual pigment. It is possible that the subsequent detection by the cell of this chemical change is similar to the detection of chemical substances by the receptor cells involved in taste and smell and by the receptor cells sensitive to chemical substances within the body. The mechanism whereby the cells of the olfactory mucous membrane of the nose detect and identify the odorous quality of substances is not known, but it is clear that in some species the receptors are very sensitive and that the capacity for discrimination of stimuli is great. It has recently been proposed (Amoore 1964) that it is the overall molecular shape that determines the ability of substances to stimulate olfactory receptors and that there are five basic shapes to which a given molecule is compared. There is some evidence in favour of this idea, but, even if it is correct, the underlying mechanism remains obscure.

5. Non-nervous structures ancillary to the receptors

5.1. *The Pacinian corpuscle*

The sensitivity of the Pacinian corpuscle to mechanical deformation is unimpaired when the membranous layers surrounding the sensory nerve ending are removed. However, the time course of the receptor potential is changed markedly by this procedure. When the intact corpuscle is subjected to a sustained compression, the receptor potential rises to a maximum in about 2 msec and decays to zero with a time constant of 3–5 msec. After removal of the lamellae surrounding the sensory nerve terminal the receptor potential evoked by a sustained compression lasts some 70 msec (Loewenstein and Mendelson 1965). Decay in the response of sense organs to sustained stimulation has been known for a long time (Adrian 1928) and is called adaptation. The time constant with which this decay proceeds varies widely for different sense organs. It would appear that in the case of the Pacinian corpuscle the mechanism that produces this decay resides largely in the mechanical properties of the lamellated capsule. This view is sustained by the analysis of a theoretical model of the elastic and viscous properties of a series of concentric elastic membranes interconnected by fine elastic connections and filled with fluid (Loewenstein and Skalak 1966). The model is set up with the spatial dimensions of a typical corpuscle, the fluid viscosity of water and the modulus of elasticity typical of biological elastic tissue. In general terms the model describes the high-pass filter that would account for the phenomenon of adaptation. In particular, the time constants of the decay of the receptor potential can be predicted provided certain assumptions are made to relate the computed core pressure to the current flowing through the receptor-cell membrane.

5.2. *The eye*

An optical image is cast onto the retina by a lens system whose geometrical optics were analysed in detail by Helmholtz and presented in the first volume of his treatise on physiological optics. Recent years have seen the application of transfer-function methods to the analysis of the quality of optical systems (Lamberts *et al.* 1958, Lamberts 1958) and these methods have been applied to the optical system of the human eye (Westheimer and Campbell 1962, Krauskopf 1962, Westheimer 1963, Campbell and Gubisch 1966).

There are two ways in which the transfer function of an optical system can be expressed: in the spatial intensity domain it is the spatial distribution of light in the image of an infinitesimally thin line object; in the spatial frequency domain it is the attenuation in modulation of a spatial sinusoidal grating expressed as a function of spatial frequency. Both methods have been applied to the eye. In practice the measurements involve throwing an image onto the fundus at the back of the eye and examining the light distribution of the aerial image formed by the light emerging from the eye. The fundus is assumed to be a nearly perfect diffusing reflector. This assumption has been shown to be valid by Campbell and Gubisch (1966) although polarization is largely retained. The distribution of light in the aerial image is the result of two traverses through the eye. The effect of a single traverse can be derived from this by computation.

The performance of any optical system is limited by diffraction, the effect being dependent on aperture and wavelength. The ideal diffraction-limited performance of the eye can be calculated with various pupil sizes for light of any spectral composition. The earlier investigations show that for pupil sizes under 3 mm the line-spread function of the eye is about twice as wide as the ideal diffraction-limited optical system, the relative performance becoming progressively worse than this as the pupil diameter is increased to 6 mm. In the most recent measurements (Campbell and Gubisch 1966) the performance of the eye with a 1·5 mm pupil is shown to be very close to the performance of an ideal optical system. Technical improvements in the experimental method can account for this discrepancy. As these measurements necessarily only set an upper bound to the spread of light in the eye, these later observations would seem to be acceptable.

The performance of the eye decreases at small pupil diameters because of diffraction and at large pupil diameters on account of optical defects. The pupil diameter at which performance is optimal, and at which the line-spread function has a minimum width, is about 2·4 mm.

5.3. *The ear*

Sound, being energy in the form of movement, is detected by receptors that are sensitive to mechanical deformation. However, since the maximum transmission rate of nerve impulses along a fibre of the auditory nerve is only about 200 sec^{-1}, and pitch can be discriminated in man up to frequencies about 20 kc/s and in some animals at much higher frequencies, it follows that frequency analysis of the sound

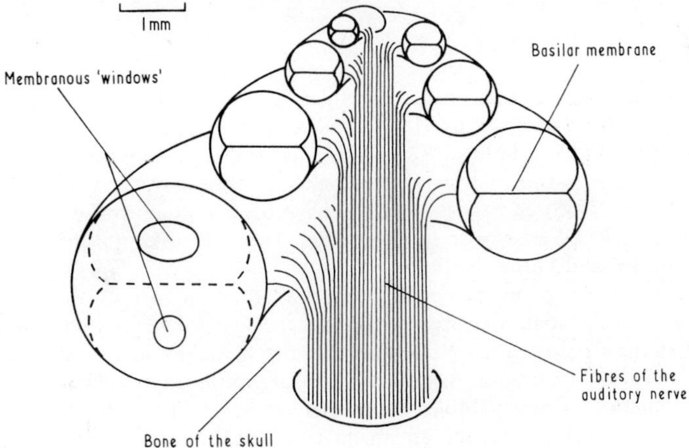

Figure 4. The cochlea seen after axial bisection.

must be performed prior to the primary transducer action. This is achieved in structures buried in the bones of the skull and called the inner ear.

The inner ear consists of a helically coiled fluid-filled tube called the cochlea. The tube is blind at one end and is divided longitudinally by a flaccid basilar membrane that terminates just short of the blind end. The 'open' end of the tube thus presents two separate sections, each of which is covered by a membrane. Sound arriving at the ear is transmitted to one of these membranous windows via a series of bony levers that act as an impedance matching device between the air-borne incident sound and the fluid-borne sound in the cochlea. Sound is conveyed from this membranous window to the other freely moving window through the cochlea fluid and across the basilar membrane. Because the acoustic impedance is frequency dependent the extent to which the sound spreads along the length of the cochlea is frequency dependent, the higher frequencies being shunted across almost directly from one window to the other, the lower frequencies occupying the whole length of the cochlea. The basilar membrane vibrates across the cochlea as the sound is transmitted through it. Placed on one side of the membrane are the sensitive structures terminating the fibres of the auditory nerve. These are known as hair cells and have fine processes projecting from their free surface. The nerve fibres emerge from the hair cells on the surface that is attached to the basilar membrane,

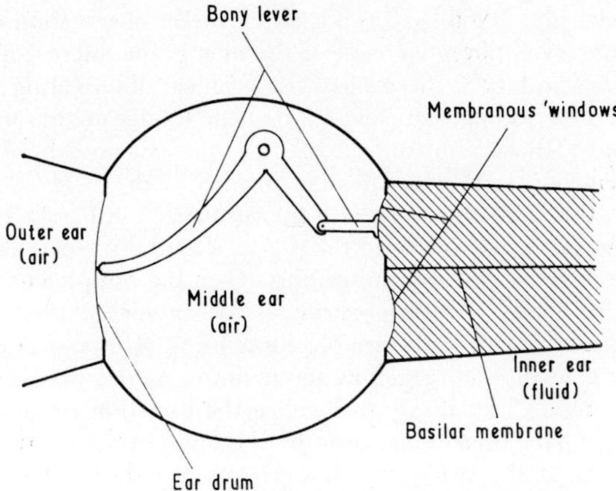

Figure 5. The functional relationships of the middle ear.

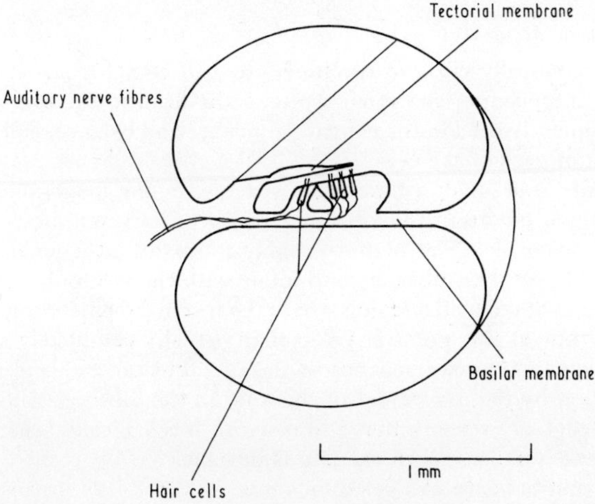

Figure 6. Transverse section of the cochlea showing detail of the structures on the basilar membrane.

and travel in the membrane towards the axis of the helix where they are gathered together to form the auditory nerve. Suspended across the top of the free ends of the hair cells is a roof-like membrane which the hairs touch during the movements of the basilar membrane. This causes deformation of the hairs and initiates impulses in the auditory nerve fibres.

The basilar membrane thus moves with the sound vibration in a manner that is frequency dependent. The membrane at the 'open' end of the cochlea vibrates with all frequencies. For a pure tone the length of basilar membrane vibrating increases with decreasing frequency. The length of membrane vibrating for a pure tone terminates sharply. This has been seen by direct observation by von Bekesy (1949 a, b) who observed the movement of the membrane microscopically through an implanted glass window in the wall of the cochlea, illuminating the membrane stroboscopically. The finding that the region of the basilar membrane that vibrates to a pure tone has a sharp point of cut-off that moves along the membrane with decreasing frequency of the tone has been confirmed by the recording of the activity of single fibres in the auditory nerve with microelectrodes (Tasaki 1954).

In general, the ear is insensitive to the phase of sound waves. The sensation of a compound tone depends only on the amplitudes of the component harmonics and not on their relative phase. This is also true of anharmonic mixtures except in so far as the mixture of two close frequencies produces beats. However, despite this, it is clear that the ear transmits information about timing rather precisely, particularly of transients of sound. The ability to localize the direction from which sound is coming depends, in part, on a comparison by the brain of the relative timing of the arrival of the sound at the two ears. The precision with which direction can be judged suggests that timing of a transient is transmitted to the brain with an accuracy not worse than 100 μsec.

5.4. *The vestibular apparatus*

Situated anatomically close to the inner ear is a complex structure concerned with signalling the position and movements of the head to the brain. This information is subsequently used in the control of posture and balance, and in the control of the direction of gaze of the eyes.

This structure consists of a fluid-filled space with one main compartment, the vestibule. Opening out from the vestibule are three narrow tubes, approximately semicircular in shape, lying in planes roughly mutually orthogonal. The bore at both ends of each of these tubes is continuous with the vestibular space. Each of the three tubes has at one end a region where the internal diameter increases slightly and across the tube at this point is a flap that virtually completely seals the tube. The flap normally lies transversely across the tube but can be displaced elastically from that position by the movement of the fluid in the tube. Passing into the flap at its attached edge are sensory nerve fibres with mechanically sensitive terminals that initiate nerve impulses when the flap is deviated.

Within the vestibule are two gelatinous masses, the otolith organs, in which are embedded crystals of calcium salts that make the density of these masses greater than that of the fluid bathing them. They are attached to regions of the vestibular wall that lie roughly at right angles to each other. In the regions of attachment are buried mechanically sensitive nerve terminals.

A theoretical model of the behaviour of the fluid in the semicircular canals has been described by van Egmond *et al.* (1949) that takes into account the viscosity of the fluid, the elasticity of the flap, and the possibility of a small amount of leakage past the flap. They arrive at the conclusion that the movement of the flap is equivalent to that of a heavily damped torsion pendulum. The device is therefore ballistic and, for rapid movements of the head, the deviation of the flap will be a measure of the angle through which the head has turned. During a period of zero or uniform angular velocity following a transient, the effect of the transient would

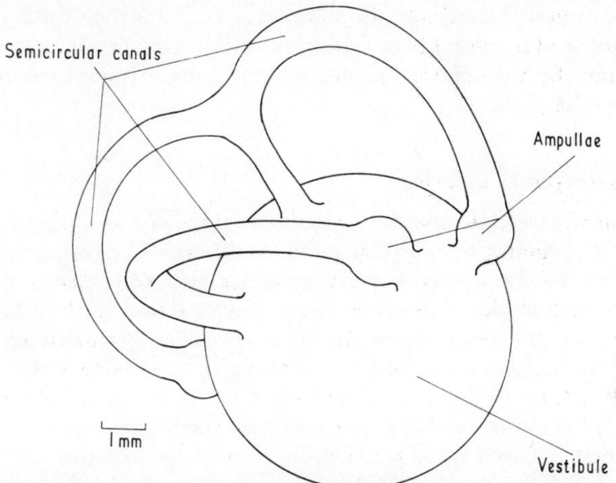

Figure 7. The vestibular apparatus.

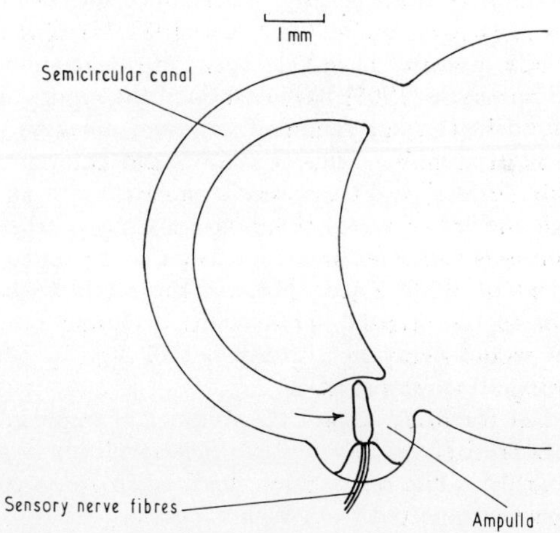

Figure 8. Longitudinal section of a semicircular canal.

decay with a time constant of about 40 sec. These predictions have been confirmed by investigating the impulse patterns in nerve fibres arising from the semicircular canals in the thornback ray (Groen *et al.* 1952).

The function of the otolith organs of the same fish have been investigated by Lowenstein and Roberts (1949). The otolith organs in this fish differ from those in man in that there is a third mass present in the vestibule. The impulse frequency in single fibres arising from these organs was measured at various orientations of the head. In general, the impulse frequency was a maximum in the case of one orientation of the head and a minimum when rotated 180° about a horizontal axis. However, among the fibres originating from any one otolith organ could be found some whose position of maximum impulse frequency was the position of minimum impulse frequency for other fibres arising from the same organ. The utilization of this information by the central nervous system must involve some sorting out of the nerve-impulse pattern.

6. Stimulus-response relations

A classical observation in psychophysics is that, as a stimulus is increased in magnitude, the magnitude of the change in that stimulus that is just detectable also increases. Weber's law asserts that the just-detectable difference is indeed proportional to the magnitude of the stimulus. Weber's law is almost certainly not precisely true for any sensory modality, but for most systems it represents their behaviour fairly well in non-extreme conditions. The reduction of sensitivity with increasing level that Weber's law describes could occur anywhere in the sensory pathway but measurements of the relationship of the response to the strength of the stimulus in many sense organs suggest that it is these structures that account for most of this non-linearity. For Weber's law to be precisely obeyed a sense organ would have to generate a frequency of impulses proportional to the logarithm of the intensity of the stimulus and this relation was claimed for both the muscle spindle and the *Limulus* eye in early researches (Matthews 1931, Hartline and Graham 1932). Recently more precise measures have been made of this relationship.

Werner and Mountcastle (1965) have examined the input–output relations of a receptor organ found in the hairy skin of cats and monkeys that is exquisitely sensitive to mechanical stimuli. These receptors can be seen, with little magnification, on the skin surface, and they were stimulated with an electromechanical transducer through the intact skin. When these sensory organs are indented, a train of nerve impulses is generated at a frequency that is greatest initially, decaying with a time constant of about 2 sec. Most of the receptors had an output that decayed to zero or to the original spontaneous discharge rate during sustained indentation; a few would decay to a steady rate of impulse generation sustained during stimuli lasting 30 sec or more.

It was found that for brief stimuli the number of impulses produced by the stimulus was rather precisely proportional to the magnitude of the stimulus raised to a power of about 0·5. The relationship deviated in a systematic way from the logarithmic relationship expected from Weber's law.

Stevens (1957) has argued that a power law describes the psychophysical relationship between stimulus strength and the perceived response better than Weber's logarithmic relationship does. Werner and Mountcastle suggest from this and from their data that transmission from the sense organ through the complexities of the central nervous system results in a transformation that overall is linear.

The exponent of the power law was independent of the duration of the stimulus. However, those units that had a response that continued for longer than the first few seconds yielded a value for the exponent close to 1·0. It is possible that these units are members of a different class of organ.

The relationship between the magnitude of the receptor potential and the intensity of illumination of the eye of *Limulus* has recently been investigated by Fuortes and Hodgkin (1964). Their analysis rises above the level of curve fitting; they propose a simple model that accounts for several different properties of this receptor potential.

They examined the receptor potentials generated by small incremental flashes superimposed on backgrounds of different illumination. In accord with a system approximately following Weber's law they found that increasing the background illumination reduced the size of the receptor potential. They also found that the time course of the receptor potential was changed by the background, the response being earlier and shorter with the more intense backgrounds. This is in agreement with the conclusions from human psychophysical experiments that sensitivity and time resolution are reciprocally related. They found that a 200-fold decrease in sensitivity was accompanied by about a twofold decrease in duration. The model that they propose which will behave in this manner is suggested by the human psychophysical observation that the threshold for seeing sinusoidal fluctuations in intensity rises very steeply with increasing frequency above a certain frequency level (De Lange 1958). This would be the case if the visual system contained a multi-stage low-pass filter. De Lange estimates the number of successive single *RC* stages that need to be present to account for the sharpness of attenuation with frequency to be about 10. Fuortes and Hodgkin point out that the effect of light on the receptor potential could be explained in terms of such a filter if light produces a decrease in leakage resistance of all the stages of the filter. A decrease in this resistance R would cause a decrease in the time scale proportional to R and an increase in the attenuation due to the filter proportional to R^{n-1}, where n is the number of stages. They estimate n by two independent methods. The relationship of the magnitude of the receptor potential to its time constants gives a value of n between 8 and 10. Fitting the shape of the rising front of the receptor potential to the output of a multi-stage filter gives a best match to a filter with 10 stages. Two further phenomena that Fuortes and Hodgkin interpret in terms of this model are the shape of the initial transient in the receptor potential evoked by large flashes and the after-effects of the exposure to light on the size and shape of the receptor potential. We shall deal with these when we come to consider the temporal properties of sense organs.

Elegant as it is, the Fuortes–Hodgkin model gives no indication of how such a multi-stage filter might be realized in the structure of the *Limulus* eye.

The decreasing sensitivity of the rods of the human eye with increasing illumination has been investigated by Rushton (1965 d). He suggests three possibilities for the mechanism whereby the eye becomes less sensitive. Either the quantum-catching power of the receptors declines, or each receptor needs to catch a greater number of quanta to generate a signal or more signals need to be generated for seeing. He argues that the last of these is the case from the following evidence. The background level of illumination that is needed to raise the threshold to three times the absolute threshold is so low that less than 1% of them would have absorbed one quantum. Yet since the threshold was raised to that extent by these 1% of rods, they must affect the threshold of the 99% that do not absorb quanta from the background. This suggests that the threshold is affected at a point where signals from many rods are pooled. This notion is substantiated by experiments with brighter backgrounds in which the background illumination consisted of a grating, each stripe of which subtends as much as 0·25° at the eye. The test flash was another grating of the same spatial frequency. The increment threshold was determined when the test flash was presented in phase and out of phase with the background and found to be the same. This was still true when the possibility of eye movements invalidating the result was eliminated. Rushton concludes that whenever a rod catches a quantum it generates a signal, that a test flash is seen when n signals arrive at the summation pool within a short time, and that the number n depends upon the time distribution of the signal flux to the pool but not upon its space distribution.

We have been considering the properties of sense organs with respect to the intensity of their stimuli. We shall now consider the way in which they behave as a function of time.

7. Temporal properties of sense organs

7.1. *Adaptational properties*

It is a general property of sense organs that when subjected to a sustained stimulus their response decays in intensity, either to zero or to some low steady level. This generalization was made by Adrian (1928). The process of decay is known as adaptation. Sense organs were shown by Adrian to adapt at different rates: muscle spindles are very slowly adapting and skin receptors of light touch and hair movement are relatively rapidly adapting. The nerve fibre is an example of extreme rapidity of adaptation; a sustained electric current passed between two electrodes placed on a nerve generates only one nerve impulse at the moment the current is switched on.

We have seen that, in general, sense organs generate a receptor potential when stimulated and that this potential is associated with currents passing through the emergent nerve fibres in a direction suitable for the initiation of nerve impulses. These nerve impulses are generated at a frequency that represents the magnitude of the receptor potential at the time of their generation. It follows that the region of nerve fibres in association with receptor cells differs from regions of nerve fibres in the course of a nerve trunk in that adaptation near the sensory receptor must be slow if it is there at all.

The adaptation of sense organs may, to a small extent, be attributable to nerve-fibre adaptation (Nakajima 1964). However, it appears that the receptor potential itself decays with time. In the case of the Pacinian corpuscle we have seen that some of this decay is explicable in terms of the mechanical properties of the corpuscle (Loewenstein and Skalak 1966). The frequency of impulses in the fibres of the skin receptors studied by Werner and Mountcastle (1964) dropped from its initial maximum value reaching a lower level 100 msec after the start of stimulation. This lower frequency level remained constant for a period of about 500 msec. Thereafter the frequency dropped again to zero, or, in a small number of units, to a low steady level. The period between 100 msec and 500 msec during which the frequency remained constant they call the early steady state. This phenomenon has not been demonstrated in other sense organs and it is possibly a property of the mechanical structure of the receptor and of the overlying skin.

Receptors in the skin sensitive to temperature changes have been investigated by Zotterman and his colleagues (see Zotterman 1953) and show marked adaptation. It is possible here also that some of this adaptation is a property of the non-nervous structures of the receptor. If the sensitive structures are responding to temperature gradients, then these will decay as thermal equilibrium is reached.

With the exception of these few cases where adaptation can in part be assigned to the physical properties of non-nervous structures in the sense organ, sensory adaptation is a property generated by the excitable components. By sacrificing fidelity in this way the nervous system achieves two advantages. Firstly, there is economy in transmission of information if a system signals only the changes in a message that is unchanging for most of the time. Secondly, in a system in which transmission delays are long compared with its best temporal resolution, some compensation for these delays is gained by transmitting rate-of-change information.

In the visual system the term adaptation is reserved for a different phenomenon which will be described later. An effect analogous to sensory adaptation is demonstrable in human vision in certain circumstances. Normally human eyes are continually performing small movements so that the image is moving slightly over the retina. If the image is not uniformly bright, this movement causes temporal fluctuations in the intensity of illumination of any point on the retina, and counteracts any adaptive process. Riggs *et al.* (1953) fitted a contact lens to the eye in such a way that the two moved together. The contact lens carried part of an optical system so designed that, should the eye move, the retinal image would move with it, remaining stabilized in position on the retina. When this is done it is found that sharp contours in the visual field become increasingly blurred and eventually disappear in a few seconds. The adaptive effect obtained by stabilizing the retinal image in this way could occur anywhere in the visual pathway, but it is likely that it takes place in the retina. The ganglion cells in the retinae of cats and rabbits show a similar rapid adaptation.

A system such as this, in which an adaptive retina is prevented from adapting by small eye movements may seem to confer little biological advantage, but could arise if adaptation is an incidental property of the detector. However, there are certain images on the retina that remain in a fixed position, such as the shadows of the retinal blood vessels and the after-images of previous exposure to light. Sensory adaptation helps to make these less conspicuous.

The response of the *Limulus* eye to the onset of bright illumination shows an initial peak in the receptor potential accompanied by a high frequency of nerve impulses. The receptor potential and the impulse frequency then decay to a lower steady level. Fuortes and Hodgkin (1964) have incorporated this phenomenon into their model. The effect of steady illumination in that model is to reduce the leakage resistance in a series of stages of a multi-stage low-pass filter. They suggest that this is not a direct effect of light on the detector but an effect produced by feedback of the output of the system. Thus, at the transient, when bright light is switched on after a period of darkness, the leakage resistance is high and the attenuation of the filter small, giving an initial phase of the receptor potential that is large and proportional to the light intensity. This large output then, in some way, causes a reduction in the leakage resistance thereby increasing the attenuation, reducing the receptor potential to a final value determined by the feedback conditions.

The term dark adaptation is used to describe another transient or non-equilibrium state in vision. We have already seen that, when in equilibrium with a certain background illumination, the sensitivity of the visual system is lower the higher the intensity of the background illumination. After exposure to light, the threshold of vision of a flash against a totally dark background does not return immediately to its low level. The threshold drops over a period of about 30 minutes before it reaches its minimum. This slow recovery of sensitivity is called dark adaptation.

Crawford (1947) introduced an interesting concept into the understanding of dark adaptation. He showed that the time course of the recovery of sensitivity after returning to the dark was not independent of the nature of the testing flash. For example, it depended on the size of the area being illuminated by the test flash, which suggests that the neural organization of the retina is changing during dark adaptation. He also showed that the raising of the incremental threshold with increasing background illumination was dependent on the nature of the testing flash. He suggested the important notion that during the course of dark adaptation the eye behaved as though it were illuminated by a background of light that fades as adaptation proceeds. He substantiated this notion by showing that at any moment during dark adaptation the thresholds of flashes covering different-sized areas were raised by just the amounts by which the thresholds of similar flashes were raised in the presence of a certain background illumination. Crawford introduced the concept of 'equivalent background' and showed that the fading of the equivalent background during dark adaptation was independent of the nature of the test flash. These observations have been confirmed and extended by Blakemore and Rushton (1965).

Barlow and Sparrock (1964) followed up Crawford's notion of equivalent backgrounds by suggesting that the equivalent background could actually be seen in the dark after exposure to light and, in fact, constituted the familiar phenomenon of the after-image. They point out that the reason why after-images appear to decay much too rapidly to account for the time course of dark adaptation could be because the after-image is fixed in position on the retina and is therefore subject to the fading associated with stabilized retinal images. They confirmed this view experimentally in two ways. They produced adjacent visual fields, one of which was a fading after-image and the other a stabilized retinal image whose illumination they could vary until the two regions matched. They showed firstly that, when measured in terms of the brightness of a matching retinal image, the after-image fades during 30 min in a way that follows the dark adaptation curve. They also showed that the thresholds of incremental flashes were the same at all times in the two matched regions.

Campbell and Rushton (1955), having developed a method of retinal densitometry whereby they could measure the extent to which rhodopsin was bleached in the intact human eye, showed that after exposure to a bleaching light the rhodopsin regenerated in the dark at a rate comparable in magnitude with the rate at which the threshold of the rods dropped during the same period of dark adaptation. The range over which these measurements could be made was limited because, in the early stages of dark adaptation, the threshold of seeing by cones is lower than the threshold of seeing by rods. Rushton (1961) overcame this difficulty by repeating the observations in a subject who suffered from a congenital deficiency of cone vision. In this study, extended over a wider range of thresholds, Rushton showed that the amount of bleached rhodopsin was linearly related to the logarithm of the visual threshold. This relationship cannot be precise because, whereas the regeneration of rhodopsin in the dark after bleaching proceeds along a predestined course, the course of recovery of sensitivity during this period depends upon the nature of the testing stimulus. However, if we substitute an equivalent background for the visual threshold and allow for the existence of an equivalent background even in a state of total dark adaptation, a linear relationship holds (Blakemore and Rushton 1965) between the logarithm of the luminous background and the quantity of bleached rhodopsin. The existence of an equivalent background in total dark adaptation derives from Fechner's century-old suggestion of an intrinsic light of the eye and from Barlow's (1957) concept of intrinsic receptor noise that we shall discuss later in this article.

Thus, we see that, during the course of dark adaptation, rhodopsin is as yet incompletely regenerated, that an equivalent background is present that can be seen as brightly as a stabilized retinal image, and that the threshold to test flashes is raised. The attractive hypothesis suggests itself that bleached rhodopsin causes the after-image and the threshold is raised because the test flash falls on the after-image acting as a luminous background.

Rushton (1965 e) has presented evidence that leads him to reject this hypothesis. He has shown that real light and equivalent background light behave differently when they are not distributed evenly over the retina. He uses a real background of an array of luminous circles and an equivalent background generated by producing an after-image of a similar array. He finds that a real background of this sort raises the threshold by just the amount that it would have been raised if the same amount of light had been evenly distributed over the retina. On the other hand, when an unevenly distributed after-image was produced in this way, the threshold was raised by an amount equal to that which would have been produced had the same amount of bleaching been evenly distributed over the retina. With real backgrounds unevenly lit the rise in the logarithm of the threshold is related to the logarithm of the average background; with after-images the rise in the logarithm threshold is related to the average of the logarithm—which is very different.

Rushton proposes a model that bears some similarity to the model that Fuortes and Hodgkin have proposed for *Limulus* eye. In this model the total real light flux is signalled to the brain through a system whose attenuation is under the control of its own output. The feedback relations are such that the overall transformation of this attenuator system is approximately logarithmic. When bleaching is present the average amount of bleached rhodopsin is also signalled to the system and combines additively with the output of the attenuator system. This combined signal does two things: it is the signal that controls the attenuation and it is the signal that represents brightness and is transmitted to the brain. The implications of this model are fully explored by Rushton (1965 f).

7.2. *Resolution and summation*

A linear system can be described with equal validity and completeness either in terms of its response to transients or in terms of its response to harmonics. The choice depends only on the way in which certain characteristics are emphasized. In a non-linear system neither method suffices to give a complete description of the system's behaviour, and the value of using both is increased. However, physiological tradition gives precedence to the analysis of transients and examples of harmonic analysis are rare.

The frequency response of sense organs shows certain general features that differ only in their time constants in different modalities. The Pacinian corpuscle (Sato 1961), the muscle spindle (Stuart *et al.* 1965) and the visual system (De Lange 1958) all show band-pass frequency characteristics. At the low-frequency end there is a gentle fall-off of response with decreasing frequency with a slope not greater than 6 dB/octave. This is the equivalent in the frequency domain of the adaptational properties described above. At the high-frequency end there is a steep fall-off of response with frequency which may reach 30 dB/octave or more. This high-frequency characteristic defines the upper limits of temporal resolution. The response of sense organs to brief stimuli containing mainly frequencies in the higher ranges is ballistic, the magnitude of the response being dependent on the time integral of the stimulus. In the visual system this ballistic property has been studied extensively and is described by the term temporal summation. The eye is non-linear in that its time constants are dependent on the level of illumination, decreasing with increasing illumination. This has been shown in the case of rectangular-wave incremental flashes by Barlow (1958) and in the case of sinusoidal modulation by De Lange (1958).

The temporal properties of the eye also depend on the spatial properties of the stimulus in a way that will be described later.

8. Spatial properties

The two sensory systems in which the spatial distribution of the stimulus is of interest are the eye and the skin. Both these systems show the spatial equivalent of the temporal property of giving emphasis to change. The subjective intensification of boundaries between regions of the visual field of different intensity was described by Ernst Mach. In the retina of the cat it has been shown (Kuffler 1953, Barlow *et al.* 1957) that certain ganglion cells have the property that they are responsive to a small spot of light over a fairly large receptive field. However, when the spot of light is in the centre of the field the cells respond when the light is switched on, and when in the periphery of the field they respond when the light is switched off. Other cells respond when the light is switched off in the centre of the field, and on in the periphery. Illuminating both the central and peripheral parts of the cell's receptive field simultaneously produces little response. This phenomenon is known as lateral inhibition and would produce the effect of reducing the activity from regions of uniform illumination and increasing activity from regions of irregular illumination. In the cat, the fringe of inhibition disappears at low levels of background illumination. This change in behaviour has been shown not to be related to a change from cone to rod vision but to be a change in the neural organization of the retina.

Lateral inhibition has also been demonstrated in the retina of the frog (Barlow 1953) and between neighbouring ommatidia in the eye of *Limulus* (Hartline *et al.* 1952).

Touch receptors in the skin have also been shown to inhibit the activity of neighbouring receptors. The analogy with the eye has been drawn by von Bekesy (1960).

Summation of light falling over an area of retina occurs in a way that resembles the summation of light falling over a period of time. Barlow (1958) has shown that the extent over which spatial summation occurs, in which the threshold drops in inverse proportionality to the area stimulated, increases as the level of background illumination is reduced. This, too, is the result of neural reorganization.

9. Spatio-temporal interaction

There is a close similarity between the spatial and the temporal properties of the retina. Furthermore, these properties are not mutually independent. Barlow (1958) has shown that the extent of spatial summation depends on the duration of the flash and the extent of temporal summation depends on its area. The relationship is reciprocal in that spatial summation is greatest when the duration is short, and temporal summation is greatest when the area of the flash is small. It seems that in some way summation in time and in space are mutually restrictive.

Another spatio-temporal interaction has been demonstrated in the eye by Alpern (1953). He has shown that the threshold of a region of retina can be raised by a flash presented to another region at a moment some 50 msec after the test flash. This effect, which can be produced either in rods or in cones but not in a way such that rods and cones interact with each other (Alpern 1965), illustrates that the sensitivity of the retina is dependent on other retinal events that may not be coincident either in time or in space.

A spatio-temporal interaction of a different sort can be seen in the demonstration by Barlow and Hill (1963) and Barlow *et al.* (1964) that there are ganglion cells in the retina of the rabbit that are specifically sensitive to velocity. These cells respond only when a spot of light is made to move over their receptive fields. The response is maximal for movement in a particular direction and zero for movement in the opposite direction. The preferred direction is constant for any one cell at any part of its receptive field, but varies from cell to cell. The magnitude of the response is virtually independent of the intensity of the light, and can be evoked by a white spot moving through a black background or vice versa.

10. Colour vision

Although the subject of colour vision is rather specialized for a general article of this sort, it has attracted considerable attention from sensory physiologists and justifies a short note on recent developments.

Brindley (1960, chap. 7) has presented the evidence that has accumulated in favour of the Young–Helmholtz view that colour discrimination has three degrees of freedom. He develops the idea that the visual pathway, at some point, contains only three univariant channels. The physical realization of these three channels might be at any point in the visual pathway. The possibilities are that there are only three visual pigments concerned with colour vision, or that there are only three types of receptor containing more than three pigments, or that there are more than three types of receptor but that the visual pathway narrows to three channels more centrally. Brindley weighs the evidence and presents the view that there are probably not more than three pigments concerned in the discrimination of colour. This is independent of the question of whether there are three types of receptor, each containing one of the three pigments. Brindley argues that, in fact, each pigment is alone present in one type of cell from evidence concerning the effect of a bleaching adapting light on colour matches. If pigments are bleached by the adapting light to an extent sufficient to alter the degree of screening that they exert, then the effect of bleaching to this extent will depend on whether they screen the light arriving at other pigments or only the light arriving at the identical pigments.

The view that there are three pigments each contained within its own type of receptor has now derived powerful support from the microspectrophotometric measurements of Marks (1965) on single cones of the retina of the goldfish. He has overcome the technical problem of obtaining the spectral absorption curve of a small quantity of a photolabile pigment that is being bleached away by the light needed to make the measurements. When the difference spectra he obtains, i.e. the spectral change induced by bleaching, are plotted superimposed on the same graph it is clear that they fall into three defined groups, each with a shape characteristic of visual pigments (Dartnall 1952), with maxima at 450, 530 and 620 nm.

The existence of three types of receptor, each with a characteristic spectral sensitivity determined by the quantum-catching power of the pigment within it, is thus fairly well established. The way in which the responses of the receptor cells are conveyed to the central nervous system is far from clear. The spectral sensitivity curves of ganglion cells under conditions of cone vision are not easily related to the action spectra of visual pigments (see Brindley 1960, p. 80 *et seq.*). Svaetichin (1953) and Svaetichin and MacNichol (1958) have described remarkable potential changes recordable with microelectrodes in the retina of the tench. These potentials, arising in unidentified structures, are coincident with illumination, and have a magnitude that is dependent on intensity. Changing the wavelength of the stimulus also changes the magnitude of these potentials and, in many cases, can also change their sign. The spectral sensitivities of these potential changes fall into a small number of different types. Naka and Rushton (1966 a) have investigated these unidentified units by superimposing spectral flashes on steady adapting lights. They have shown that the response of these units can be explained in terms of two pigments, one of which depolarizes and the other hyperpolarizes. One type of unit behaves as though one of its pigments is the same as Marks's pigment with its maximum at 540 nm, and the other probably Marks's pigment with its maximum at 450 nm. Another type of unit behaves as though one of its pigments is the same as Marks's pigment 540 nm, and the other a pigment with an action spectrum maximum at 680 nm which does not coincide with the pigment that Marks found in the red, peaking at 620 nm. Naka and Rushton (1966 b) consider whether this apparent pigment with the action spectrum maximum at 680 nm could be mimicked by the interaction of two other pigments. They show that, whereas the action spectrum could be that of a pseudo-pigment of this sort, its response to mixtures of spectral colours would differ from that of a true pigment. In this way they show that the action spectrum peaking at 680 nm is that of a true pigment and suggest that it has escaped detection in difference spectrum measurements because it behaves as an unbleachable sensitizer.

11. Noise

Katz (1950 a) remarked on the irregularity of impulses that arise from an unstretched muscle spindle and suggested that this might arise either from molecular agitation in the mechanical receptor substance or from ionic noise in the terminal membrane. Fatt and Katz (1952) have pursued the matter of thermal noise in nervous structures and calculate that the effect on the membrane potential will be inversely related to the size of the cells. Buller *et al.* (1953) have analysed the distribution of impulses arising from the frog's muscle spindle. They applied two tests of randomness to the intervals between successive nerve impulses: the standard deviation of the distribution would be equal to the mean, and the distribution would be exponential. They showed these tests to be satisfied in the case of the impulse distribution at low frequency obtained from the relaxed spindle. If the frequency of impulses were increased by stretching the muscle spindle, then the distribution of impulses became more orderly. Buller (1965) has shown that the impulse patterns are consistent with the behaviour of a spindle that emits impulses at a frequency directly proportional to the generator potential when that potential is subject to a constant amount of noise. He also points out that the magnitude of the noise is compatible with the magnitude of noise calculated as possible by Fatt and Katz.

A similar property has been demonstrated in the pattern of nerve impulses recorded in fibres arising from the carotid body of the cat (Biscoe and Taylor 1963). This organ is sensitive to chemical changes in the blood and is concerned in the control of respiration. In these fibres the impulse pattern satisfied the tests of randomness at low frequencies but showed increasing regularity as the frequency increased.

These results are in contrast with those obtained by Werner and Mountcastle (1964) in fibres from mechanoreceptive organs in the hairy skin of monkeys. They describe the extreme regularity of impulses in these discharges as metronome-like. Although the lowest frequency at which they calculate a standard deviation of the interval distribution is somewhat high, it seems unlikely that any severe irregularity occurs at those frequencies at which it is marked in the muscle spindle.

The problem of noise in the visual system has certain special considerations that arise out of the quantal nature of light. Hecht *et al.* (1942) had used the estimate of statistical uncertainty in their proof that one quantum suffices to excite a rod. Barlow (1957) proposes the view that the eye has developed in such a way that it establishes a criterion of constant fallibility–infallibility being impossible in a noisy system. On this basis he is able to estimate the intrinsic noise of the visual system. To this intrinsic noise is added the uncertain variation due to quantal fluctuation in the real light falling on the eye. In this way he has been able to interpret many of the properties of the absolute threshold (Barlow 1956) and show them to be consistent with some of the properties of the increment threshold under certain conditions. In particular, the assumption that the visual thresholds are determined in this way leads to the expectation that the incremental threshold should be proportional to the square root of the intensity of the background illumination. This is at variance with Weber's law, and also with the careful measurements of incremental threshold made by Aguilar and Stiles (1954). However, Barlow shows that, when the test flash is small in area and short in duration, it obeys the square-root relationship over an extended range of background intensities. He concludes that "human thresholds are efficient statistical judgments of constant fallibility in which noise—the random factor which tends to cause errors—arises from fluctuations in the number of quanta absorbed from the background light and the 'dark light'".

12. The central nervous control of sense organs

Some sense organs are supplied with nerve fibres that convey impulses from the brain centrifugally to the organ. In some cases these impulses are generated in response to events occurring in the sense organ itself, in which case they represent feedback control of the sense organ with the central nervous system in the feedback path. In other cases the central nervous system exerts a control on the sense organ in a way that is largely independent of its own activity. It will be convenient to discuss these separately.

12.1. *Feedback*

It is a familiar observation that shining a light into the eye causes the area of the pupil to get smaller, thereby tending to reduce the amount of light entering the eye. The nervous pathway involved in this response passes through the central nervous system. Looked upon as a mechanism for reducing the magnitude of variations in light intensity, the pupil response is remarkably inefficient. The maximum possible range of attenuation cannot exceed about 20 : 1 which is negligible compared with a range of at least $10^6 : 1$ in the ability of the retina itself to adjust its sensitivity to the incident illumination.

The ear has a mechanical system which can control attenuation and which is under feedback control through the central nervous system, and is thus, in some ways, analogous to the iris of the eye. In the middle ear is a series of small bones acting as a mechanical lever and transmitting sound from the outer to the inner ear. Attached to these bones are two small muscles and when these contract the stiffness of the lever system is increased. From the experiments of Galambos and Rupert (1959) on the cat, it appears that these muscles only contract consistently to intense sound stimulation. There is no clear relationship with moderate and high intensities of stimulation. It is suggested that these muscles are there to provide overload protection for the delicate structures of the inner ear. Galambos and Rupert also report sporadic irregular contraction of the muscles, uncorrelated with the incident sound intensity, so it is possible that there are other functions associated with these structures.

In addition to these mechanical devices, the iris and the middle-ear muscles, there is some evidence that some receptor cells are under direct central nervous feedback control. The best evidence for this is in the case of the ear, where Galambos (1956) has shown that electrical stimulation of certain regions of the brain reduces the neural response of the ear. This is so, even after removal of the bones of the middle ear. Galambos suggests that the effect is mediated through fibres conducting centrifugally and ending near or on the hair cells of the cochlea. Rasmussen (1955) has demonstrated the existence of such nerve fibres histologically, and has shown anatomically that at least some of these fibres form a feedback loop.

12.2. *General central control*

Whether the general state of the central nervous system can influence the sensitivity of sense organs has been the subject of much recent debate. The evidence that it does is scanty. In the case of the eye the argument has proceeded along three lines. Firstly, the histological evidence is contradictory in the cat

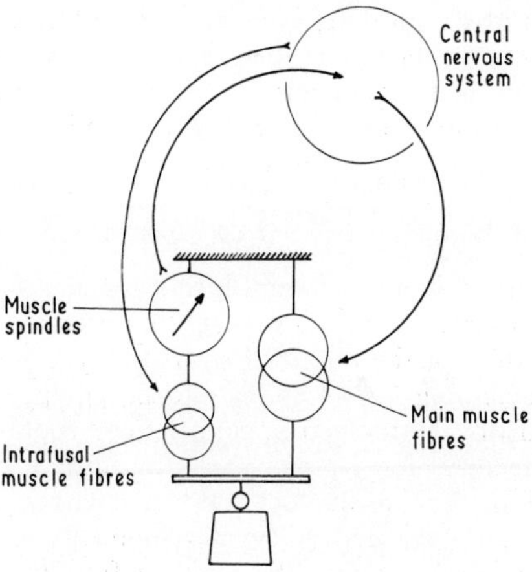

Figure 9. The muscle-spindle servo loop.

(Brooke *et al.* 1965, Brindley and Hamasaki 1966) but rather more definitely in favour of the existence of centrifugal fibres in the pigeon (Maturana and Frenk 1965). Secondly, impulses travelling peripherally have been recorded in the cat's optic nerve in certain circumstances (Spinelli *et al.* 1964). Thirdly, Brindley (1960, pp. 107–14) has argued that there is little to indicate that, if there are such impulses, they do anything physiologically.

The one sense organ that certainly does receive impulses from the central nervous system and modifies its behaviour accordingly is the muscle spindle. This organ consists of specialized muscle fibres. About half-way along their length is a region that is non-contractile and accommodates the terminals of the sensory nerves. Passive stretch of the whole muscle causes impulses to be transmitted along these sensory fibres. The contractile ends of the intrafusal muscle fibres are supplied with motor nerve fibres. When these are active and the intrafusal muscle fibres contract, the sensory region is stretched by them, and the sensory fibres transmit impulses. On the other hand, when the main muscle fibres of the muscle in which the spindle is buried contract, they relieve the spindle of stretch and reduce the frequency of impulses coming from it. The intrafusal fibres are effectively in series with the sense organ, and the main muscle fibres are in parallel. It has long been known that stretching the muscle spindle causes the main muscle fibres to contract reflexly, i.e. by a path involving the central nervous system. On the basis of these facts Eldred *et al.* (1953) have proposed an elegant hypothesis about the way in which these structures function. They suggest that in certain circumstances the central nervous system initiates a muscle contraction by activating the intrafusal muscle fibres. This excites the spindle which reflexly causes the main muscle to contract and relieve the stretch on the spindle. The spindle acts as a device for detecting a discrepancy in the length of the main muscle fibres and the intrafusal fibres and the main muscle will adjust its length to minimize this discrepancy. This is then a servo-mechanism controlling the main muscle length. As it is only the main muscle fibres that are load bearing it is suggested that this is a mechanism that makes muscle length less load dependent and less affected by fatigue. Matthews (1964, 1966) has argued powerfully against this view on several grounds. He contends that the loop gain is inadequate to be effective, and that the muscle spindles are functionally more complex than this notion demands.

13. Conclusion

Our understanding of biological transducers remains far from complete. In particular, the present state of our knowledge does little to relate the known facts about sensory function with the observed structure of sensory organs. However, the picture that is emerging shows animals to be equipped with a large set of detectors that are sensitive and selective, compact and sophisticated. Allowing for their durability and facility of self-repair these transducers stand comparison with the best products of modern technology. When it is realized that many of the products of recent technology depend on developments in materials rather than methods, and that biological systems suffer severely from the limitation of materials compatible with life, it is possible to see the developmental power that derives from the ruthless market-place of biological competition. There is no doubt that at present man can build better transducers with his genetic structure than he can with his hands and brain.

Glossary of biological terms

Action potential: the potential changes occurring during activity in a nerve or muscle

Adaptation: the property of sense organs whereby they lose their sensitivity on sustained stimulation

Axoplasm: the material within a nerve fibre

Basilar membrane: a membrane in the ear bearing the sensory elements

Cochlea: a helically coiled tube in the ear, where frequency analysis occurs

Extracellular fluid:	the fluid bathing all cells in the body outside the blood vessels
Generator potential:	the potential change occurring at sensory cells when they are stimulated
Hair cells:	sensory cells found in many locations which have short hair-like projections (bending these hairs stimulates the cell)
Intrafusal fibres:	specialized muscle fibres that run through muscle spindles (they can contract in response to impulses arriving along nerve fibres that are independent of the main nerve supply of the muscle)
Lamella:	a layer, as in the structure of a Pacinian corpuscle
Limulus:	the king crab
Medullated nerve fibre:	a nerve fibre surrounded by a fatty sheath of myelin
Metabolic activity:	the chemical processes involved in energy transfer in the body
Muscle spindle:	a sense organ found in muscles that is stimulated when the muscle is stretched
Myelin sheath:	the fatty layer around a medullated nerve fibre
Myelinated nerve fibre:	same as medullated nerve fibre
Nerve impulse:	a disturbance propagated along nerve fibres and constituting the nervous message
Node of Ranvier:	a break in the fatty sheath around medullated nerve fibres
Ommatidium:	one unit of the compound eyes of invertebrate animals
Otolith organs:	sense organs in the vestibular apparatus concerned with detecting head orientation
Pacinian corpuscle:	a mechanosensitive sense organ present abundantly in the body
Receptor cell:	a cell that converts information into a nervous form
Receptor potential:	the same as generator potential
Refractoriness:	the property of biological excitable tissues whereby their excitability is lowered in the period following activity
Retina:	the sensory and nervous layers at the back of the eye
Semicircular canals:	fluid-filled tubes situated close to the ear concerned with the detection of rotation of the head
Vertebrate:	possessing a backbone
Vestibular apparatus:	the sensory system, situated near the ear, comprising the semicircular canals and the otolith organs, concerned with detecting head orientation and movement

References

Adrian, E. D., 1926, *J. Physiol.*, **61**, 49–72.
—— 1928, *The Basis of Sensation* (London: Christophers).
Aguilar, M., and Stiles, W. S., 1954, *Optica Acta*, **1**, 59–65.
Alpern, M., 1953, *J. Opt. Soc. Amer.*, **43**, 648–57.
—— 1965, *J. Physiol.*, **176**, 462–72.
Alvarez-Buylla, R., and de Arellano, J. R., 1953, *Amer. J. Physiol.*, **172**, 237–50.

AMOORE, J. E., 1964, *Ann. N.Y. Acad. Sci.*, **116**, 457–76.
BARLOW, H. B., 1953, *J. Physiol.*, **119**, 69–88.
—— 1956, *J. Opt. Soc. Amer.*, **46**, 634–9.
—— 1957, *J. Physiol.*, **136**, 469–88.
—— 1958, *J. Physiol.*, **141**, 337–50.
BARLOW, H. B., FITZHUGH, R., and KUFFLER, S. W., 1957, *J. Physiol.*, **137**, 338–54.
BARLOW, H. B., and HILL, R. M., 1963, *Science*, **139**, 412–4.
BARLOW, H. B., HILL, R. M., and LEVICK, W. R., 1964, *J. Physiol.*, **173**, 377–407.
BARLOW, H. B., and SPARROCK, J. M. B., 1964, *Science*, **144**, 1309–14.
VON BEKESY, G., 1949 a, *J. Acoust. Soc. Amer.*, **21**, 233–45.
—— 1949 b, *J. Acoust. Soc. Amer.*, **21**, 245–54.
—— 1960, *J. Opt. Soc. Amer.*, **50**, 1060–70.
BISCOE, T. J., and TAYLOR, A., 1963, *J. Physiol.*, **168**, 332–44.
BLAKEMORE, C. B., and RUSHTON, W. A. H., 1965, *J. Physiol.* **181**, 612–28.
BRINDLEY, G. S., 1956, *J. Physiol.*, **134**, 360–84.
—— 1960, *Physiology of the Retina and the Visual Pathway* (London: Edward Arnold).
BRINDLEY, G. S., and HAMASAKI, D. I., 1966, *J. Physiol.*, **184**, 444–9.
BROOKE, R. N. L., DOWNER, J. DE C., and POWELL, T. P. S., 1965, *Nature, Lond.*, **207**, 1365–7.
BULLER, A. J., 1965, *J. Physiol.*, **179**, 402–16.
BULLER, A. J., NICHOLLS, J. G., and STRÖM, G., 1953, *J. Physiol.*, **122**, 409–18.
CALMA, I., 1965, *J. Physiol.*, **177**, 31–41.
CAMPBELL, F. W., and GUBISCH, R. W., 1966, *J. Physiol.*, **186**, 558–78.
CAMPBELL, F. W., and RUSHTON, W. A. H., 1955, *J. Physiol.*, **130**, 131–47.
CRAWFORD, B. H., 1947, *Proc. Roy. Soc.* B, **134**, 283–302.
DARTNALL, H. J. A., 1952, *J. Physiol.*, **116**, 257–89.
DE LANGE, H., 1958, *J. Opt. Soc. Amer.*, **48**, 777–89.
DENTON, E. J., 1954, *J. Physiol.*, **124**, 16–7P.
DIAMOND, J., GRAY, J. A. B., and INMAN, D. R., 1958, *J. Physiol.*, **142**, 382–94.
VAN EGMOND, A. A. J., GROEN, J. J., and JONGKEES, L. B. W., 1949, *J. Physiol.*, **110**, 1–17.
ELDRED, E., GRANIT, R., and MERTON, P. A., 1953, *J. Physiol.*, **122**, 498–523.
FATT, P., 1958, *Rep. Progr. Phys.*, **21**, 112–43 (London: Physical Society).
FATT, P., and KATZ, B., 1951, *J. Physiol.*, **115**, 320–69.
—— 1952, *Nature, Lond.*, **166**, 597–8.
FUORTES, M. G. G., and HODGKIN, A. L., 1964, *J. Physiol.*, **172**, 239–63.
FURUKAWA, T., SASAOKA, T., and HOSOYA, Y., 1959, *Jap. J. Physiol.*, **9**, 143–52.
GALAMBOS, R., 1956, *J. Neurophysiol.*, **19**, 424–37.
GALAMBOS, R., and RUPERT, A., 1959, *J. Acoust. Soc. Amer.*, **31**, 349–55.
GRAY, J. A. B., and SATO, M., 1953, *J. Physiol.*, **122**, 610–36.
GROEN, J. J., LOWENSTEIN, O., and VENDRICK, A. J. H., 1952, *J. Physiol.*, **117**, 329–46.
HARTLINE, H. K., 1938, *Amer. J. Physiol.*, **121**, 400–15.
HARTLINE, H. K., and GRAHAM, C. H., 1932, *J. Cell. Comp. Physiol.*, **1**, 277–95.
HARTLINE, H. K., WAGNER, H. G., and MACNICHOL, E. B., 1952, *Cold Spr. Harb. Symp. Quant. Biol.*, **17**, 125–41 (Cold Spring Harbour, Long Island, N.Y.: Biological Laboratory).
HECHT, S., SHLAER, S., and PIRENNE, M., 1942, *J. Gen. Physiol.*, **25**, 819–40.
HODGKIN, A. L., 1958, *Proc. Roy. Soc.* B, **148**, 1–37.
HODGKIN, A. L., and HUXLEY, A. F., 1952, *J. Physiol.*, **117**, 500–44.
HUXLEY, A. F., and STÄMPFLI, R., 1949, *J. Physiol.*, **108**, 321–39.
KATZ, B., 1950 a, *J. Physiol.*, **111**, 248–60.
—— 1950 b, *J. Physiol.*, **111**, 261–82.
KRAUSKOPF, J., 1962, *J. Opt. Soc. Amer.*, **52**, 1046–50.
KUFFLER, S. W., 1953, *J. Neurophysiol.*, **16**, 37–68.
LAMBERTS, R. L., 1958, *J. Opt. Soc. Amer.*, **48**, 490–5.
LAMBERTS, R. L., HIGGINS, G. C., and WOLFE, R. N., 1958, *J. Opt. Soc. Amer.*, **48**, 487–90.
LOEWENSTEIN, W. R., and ISHIKO, N., 1959, *Nature, Lond.*, **183**, 1724–6.
LOEWENSTEIN, W. R., and MENDELSON, M., 1965, *J. Physiol.*, **177**, 377–97.

LOEWENSTEIN, W. R., and SKALAK, R., 1966, *J. Physiol.*, **182**, 346–78.
LOEWENSTEIN, W. R., TERUZUOLO, C. A., and WASHIZU, Y., 1963, *Science*, **142**, 1180–1.
LOWENSTEIN, O., and ROBERTS, T. D. M., 1949, *J. Physiol.*, **110**, 392–415.
MACNICHOL, E. F., and SVAETICHIN, G. 1958, *Amer. J. Ophthal.*, **46**, 26–40.
MARKS, W. B., 1965, *J. Physiol.*, **178**, 14–32.
MATTHEWS, B. H. C., 1931, *J. Physiol.*, **71**, 64–110.
MATTHEWS, P. B. C., 1964, *Physiol. Rev.*, **44**, 219–88.
—— 1966, *J. Physiol.*, **184**, 450–72.
MATURANA, H. R., and FRENK, S., 1965, *Science*, **150**, 359–61.
MENDELSON, M., and LOEWENSTEIN, W. R., 1964, *Science*, **144**, 554–5.
MULLINGER, A. M., 1964, *Proc. Roy. Soc.* B., **160**, 345–59.
MURRAY, R. W., 1965, *J. Physiol.*, **180**, 592–606.
NAKA, K. I., and RUSHTON, W. A. H., 1966 a, *J. Physiol.*, **185**, 536–55.
—— 1966 b, *J. Physiol.*, **185**, 556–86.
NAKAJIMA, S., 1964, *Science*, **146**, 1168–70.
NARAHASHI, T., MOORE, J. W., and SCOTT, W. R., 1964, *J. Gen. Physiol.*, **47**, 965–74.
NISHI, K., and SATO, M., 1966, *J. Physiol.*, **184**, 376–86.
OTTOSON, D., 1964, *J. Physiol.*, **171**, 109–18.
OTTOSON, D., and SVAETICHIN, G., 1952, *Cold Spr. Harb. Symp. Quant. Biol.*, **17**, 165–73 (Cold Spring Harbour, Long Island, N.Y.: Biological Laboratory).
—— 1953, *Acta Physiol. Scand.* (*Suppl.* 106), **29**, 538–64.
DE ROBERTIS, E., 1956, *J. Biophys. Biochem. Cytol.*, **2**, 319–30.
RASMUSSEN, G. L., 1955, *Amer. J. Physiol.*, **186**, 653.
RIGGS, L. A., RATLIFF, F., CORNSWEET, J. C., and CORNSWEET, T. N., 1953, *J. Opt. Soc. Amer.*, **43**, 495–501.
RUSHTON, W. A. H., 1955, *J. Physiol.*, **129**, 41–2P.
—— 1961, *J. Physiol.*, **156**, 193–205.
—— 1963 a, *J. Physiol.*, **168**, 345–59.
—— 1963 b, *J. Physiol.*, **168**, 360–73.
—— 1963 c, *J. Physiol.*, **168**, 374–88.
—— 1965 a, *J. Physiol.*, **176**, 24–37.
—— 1965 b, *J. Physiol.*, **176**, 38–45.
—— 1965 c, *J. Physiol.*, **176**, 56–72.
—— 1965 d, *J. Physiol.*, **178**, 141–60.
—— 1965 e, *J. Physiol.*, **181**, 645–55.
—— 1965 f, *Proc. Roy. Soc.* B, **162**, 20–46.
SATO, M., 1961, *J. Physiol.*, **159**, 391–409.
SPINELLI, D. N., PRIBRAM, K. H., and WEINGARTEN, M., 1965, *Exp. Neurol.*, **12**, 303–19.
STEVENS, S. S., 1957, *Psychol. Rev.*, **64**, 153–81.
STILES, W. S., 1939, *Proc. Roy. Soc.* B, **127**, 64–105.
STUART, D., OTT, K., ISHAKAWA, K., and ELDRED, E., 1965, *Exp. Neurol.*, **13**, 82–95.
SVAETICHIN, G., 1953, *Acta Physiol. Scand.* (*Suppl.* 106), **29**, 565–600.
SVAETICHIN, G., and MACNICHOL, E. F., 1958, *Ann. N.Y. Acad. Sci.*, **74**, 385–404.
TASAKI, I., 1954, *J. Neurophysiol.*, **17**, 97–122.
TOMITA, T., 1950, *Jap. J. Physiol.*, **1**, 110–7.
WALD, G., BROWN, P. K., and SMITH, F. H., 1955, *J. Gen. Physiol.*, **38**, 623–81.
WERNER, G., and MOUNTCASTLE, V. B., 1965, *J. Neurophysiol.*, **28**, 359–97.
WESTHEIMER, G., 1963, *J. Opt. Soc. Amer.*, **53**, 86–93.
WESTHEIMER, G., and CAMPBELL, F. W., 1962, *J. Opt. Soc. Amer.*, **52**, 1040–5.
ZOTTERMAN, Y., 1953, *Ann. Rev. Physiol.*, **15**, 357–72.

First stages in the x-ray analysis of proteins

Sir LAWRENCE BRAGG

The Royal Institution, London

Abstract. The paper describes the many attempts, lasting over nearly a quarter of a century, which finally led to the analysis of the structure of a protein molecule by x rays. At each stage fragments of information about the nature of the molecule were gleaned, which encouraged the continuation of the project, but were very imperfect. There was a widespread belief that the goal was unattainable, at least in the near future, but quite suddenly a way to success was found, and myoglobin was analysed by Kendrew, and haemoglobin by Perutz.

"The structure of proteins is the major unsolved problem on the boundary of chemistry and biology to-day."

"The evidence that the x-ray study of the crystalline proteins themselves provides for the elucidation of their structure is abundant, but it is extremely difficult to interpret. Photographs of crystalline proteins show hundreds of spots and marked differences of intensities stretching right out to reflections corresponding to interatomic distances. Unfortunately, however, direct analysis of these photographs is rendered impossible by the fact that we can never know the phases of the reflections corresponding to the different spots. The ambiguity introduced in this way can only be removed by some physical artifice, *such as the introduction of a heavy atom*, or the observation of intensity changes on dehydration which have not hitherto been carried out in practice."

"The problem of protein structure is now a definite and not unattainable goal, but for success it requires a degree of collaboration between research workers which has not yet been reached."

These quotations have been taken from the report of a Discourse on the 'Structure of Proteins' given at the Royal Institution by J. D. Bernal in January 1939. The italics are mine. It is a fascinating account to read now, both as reviewing the state of knowledge at that time and as predicting the future course of research. The first pictures of diffraction by protein were, it will be remembered, observed by Bernal and Crowfoot (1934), with a crystal of pepsin, their success being due to the realization that the crystal must be kept in its mother liquid if it is to remain unaltered. X-ray analysis of protein stems from this pioneer discovery.

When I read the present paper to a meeting of the X-ray Analysis Group on 15th November 1963, I called it 'How protein structures were not worked out' because it is an account of the preliminary investigations before final success was achieved. The progress of the work may be likened to the scaling of Mount Everest. A series of camps were established at ever-increasing heights, till finally a last camp was set up from which the successful assault on the summit was made. I was closely associated with the establishment of each camp in turn up to the highest, from which those brave mountaineers Perutz and Kendrew made their final dash, and I hope that an account of those ventures, which lasted for twenty-five

PLATE I

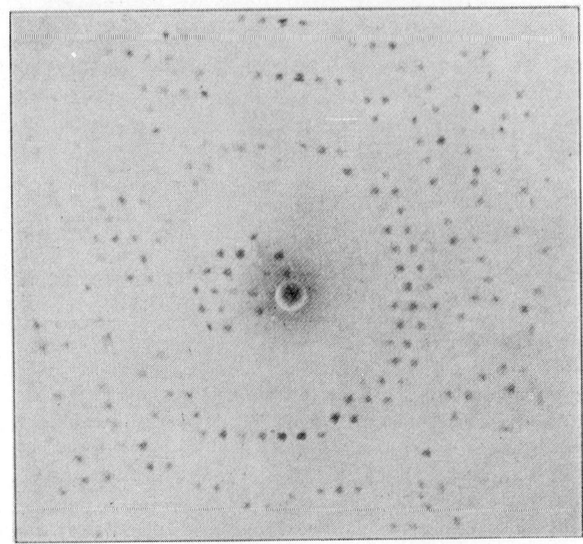

Figure 1. An early oscillation photograph of horse methaemoglobin (Bernal 1939).

years before success was achieved, will be interesting as a piece of 'scientific history'.

When I went to Cambridge in 1938 Perutz was a young student who had come to England from Vienna. Bernal, Fankuchen and Perutz (1938) had obtained fine photographs of chymotrypsin and haemoglobin, and when Perutz showed me the haemoglobin diffraction patterns I could not but be enthusiastic about their possibilities (figure 1, plate I). It was at that time difficult to get support in this country for a foreign student, but the Rockefeller Foundation came to the rescue by providing a salary for Perutz as my assistant and an annual grant for apparatus, the total being £375 a year! This was the modest beginning of the venture which has now grown into the Medical Research Council's famous laboratory at Cambridge for research into molecular biology. The war soon stopped all research, but when work was resumed again I approached the Medical Research Council for help and Sir Edward Mellanby, then secretary, backed us and so initiated the support which has been so generously continued.

It is convenient to describe the course of the work as a series of stages, the 'camps' of my mountaineering analogy.

Stage 1. 1947–49

This is represented by the papers 'An x-ray study of horse methaemoglobin, I and II' (Boyes-Watson *et al.* 1947, Perutz 1949). In the first paper Perutz, with his colleagues Boyes-Watson and Davidson, attempted to deduce the shape of the haemoglobin molecules and certain features of their internal structure from the x-ray diffraction patterns. He arrived at the 'pill-box' model shown in figure 2. The molecules are pictured as short cylinders close packed in sheets separated by sheets of water molecules, the latter feature being introduced to explain the swelling and shrinking of the crystals which Perutz had observed. Perutz conjectured that these sheets of water molecules varied in thickness in the stages of swelling and shrinking. Two-dimensional Patterson projections suggested that bundles of protein chains were arranged parallel to the *a* axis of the crystal (figure 3).

Paper II describes a three-dimensional pattern synthesis. It was a formidable task with the facilities then available; the limiting sphere out to a spacing of 2·8 Å contained some 62 700 reciprocal points, which symmetry reduced to 7840. The data were processed by an electronic computer for the first time in protein analysis. The object is described by a quotation from the paper:

"If the globin molecule consisted of a complex interlocking system of coiled polypeptide chains where interatomic vectors occur with equal frequency in all possible directions, the Patterson synthesis would be unlikely to provide a clue to the structure. On the other hand, if the polypeptide chains were arranged in layers or parallel bundles, interatomic vectors within the layer plane or in the chain direction should occur particularly frequently and should give rise to a vector structure showing a corresponding system of layers or chains, which could then be interpreted without difficulty. All the more plausible hypotheses of globular protein structure put forward in recent years have been based on systems of the latter kind (Astbury 1936, Pauling 1940). Hence it was not unreasonable to hope that the Patterson synthesis might lead to interpretable results which would justify the great effort involved in its preparation."

For a long time the idea that the molecule contained some kind of regular structure of protein chains, which would give a strongly defined character to a

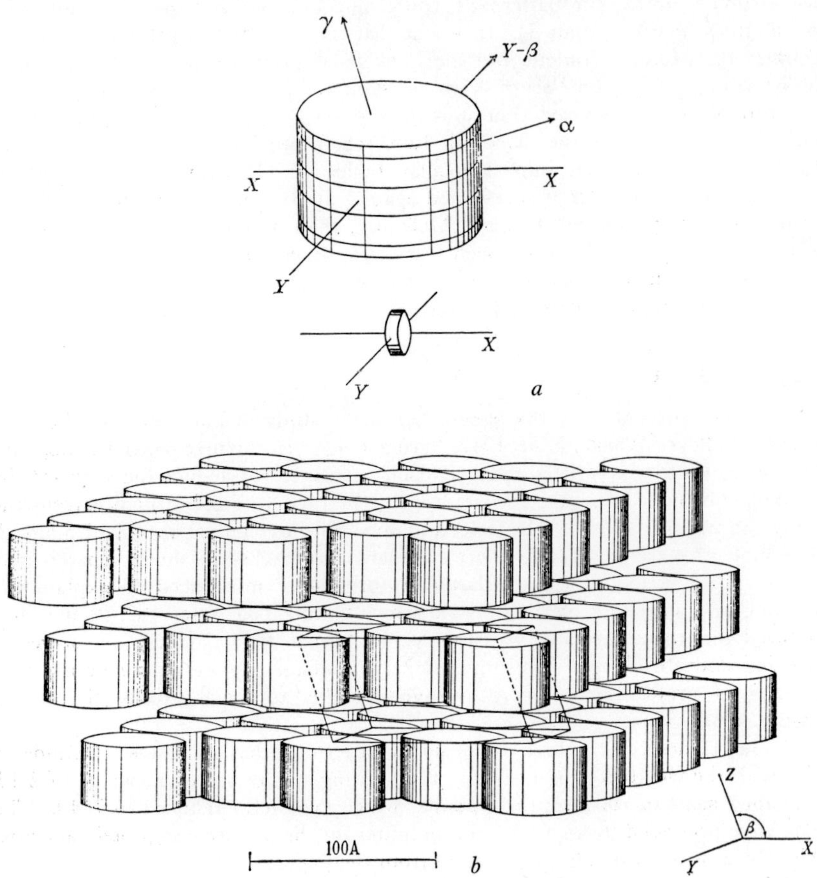

Figure 2. (*a*) The 'pill-box' model of the haemoglobin molecule, with the haem group in corresponding orientation. (*b*) The packing of the molecules, showing the water layers between them which are reduced in thickness when the crystal shrinks (Boyes-Watson *et al.* 1947).

Patterson synthesis was a guiding star which encouraged the investigations. As events turned out, it was a false star. Of the alternatives in the quotation, the first is now known to be correct. If this had been realized at the time the problem would have seemed so hopeless that the quest might well have been discouraged, but

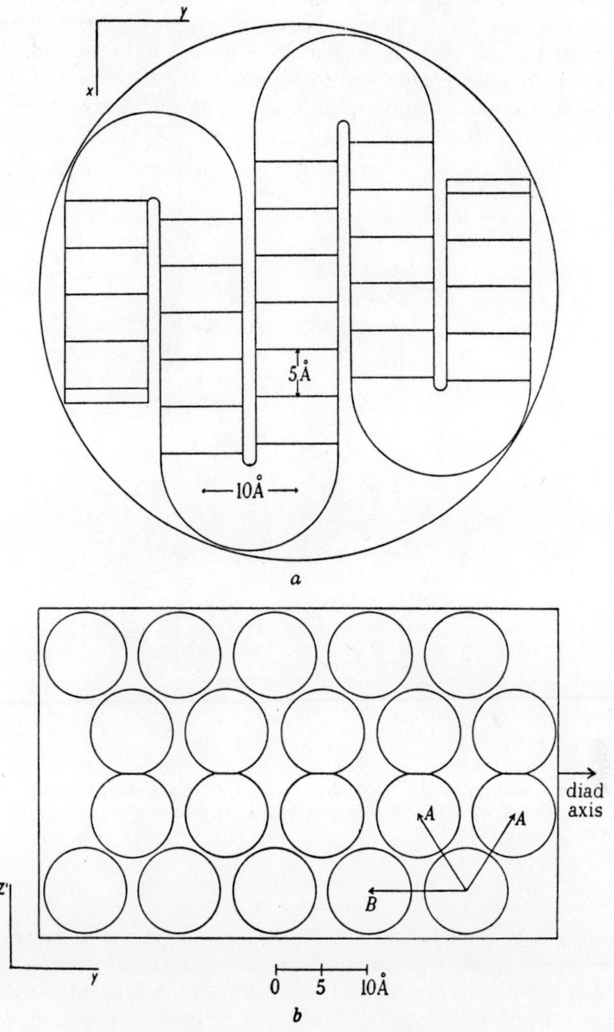

Figure 3. The run of the chains in the haemoglobin molecule, with a 5 Å repeat and a 10 Å separation (Perutz 1949).

fortunately this was not the case. The three-dimensional synthesis (figure 4) encouraged the idea that there was some kind of rod like structure parallel to the *a* axis, that "the shape of the folded chain is roughly cylindrical with an average diameter of 10·5 Å, and that there is a marked 5 Å vector of repeat along the folded chain". Actually the last two conclusions have proved to be correct, although the feature on which they were supposed to be based, the bundles of rods parallel to the *a* axis, has a very minor counterpart in the haemoglobin structure!

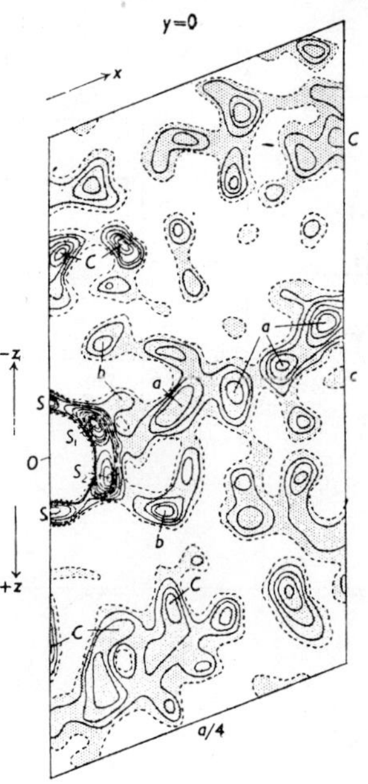

Figure 4. A central section of the three-dimensional Patterson, showing the rod of density parallel to the *a* axis which was attributed to polypeptide chains running in this direction (Perutz 1949).

Stage 2

I began to get deeply interested in Perutz's results at this stage and speculated on the form of the folded polypeptide chain. It seemed to me that Astbury's model of a kind of Greek key pattern was extremely improbable, and that a helix was a far more likely structure because it placed each amino-acid residue in the same kind of position in the chain. This was no new idea; Huggins (1943) had reviewed possible helical chains. The available data were as follows. Astbury had referred the β-keratin x-ray diagram to an extended polypeptide chain with a repeat distance of 3·4 Å. It shrinks to half its length in the α configuration, hence the average length per residue in the α chain must be 1·7 Å, giving three residues in the repeat distance of 5·1 Å indicated by the α-keratin x-ray diagram. Perutz had deduced that each folded chain in haemoglobin was surrounded by six others at distances of 10–11 Å. Assuming this close packing the number of residues in each repeat of 5·1 Å calculated from the density came to be 3·3. The three-dimensional Patterson synthesis gave strong indication of a repeat at about 5 Å. It was also regarded as very probable that the chain is held in a folded condition by hydrogen bonds between NH and CO, and that these hydrogen bonds are nearly parallel to the axis of the chain.

With these features as a basis, we tried various forms of helical chain, described in a paper by Perutz, Kendrew and myself (Bragg, Kendrew and Perutz 1950). I have always regarded this paper as the most ill-planned and abortive in which I have ever been involved. We allowed free rotation around all the single bonds in the chain

```
 O   H R  H
 ‖    \/  |
 C    C   N
/ \N/  \C/ \C/
   |    ‖  / \
   H    O H   R
```

Even when chains not conforming to the above data are discarded there still remains a maze of possibilities. I remember that we invited our chemical colleagues to look at what we felt were our most promising structures and tell us of any criterion which would make one more probable than the rest, but we completely missed the real clue. This came when Pauling's brilliant solution of the α helix with a non-integral number of residues per turn was announced (Pauling, Corey and Branson 1951). His studies of bond energies convinced him that the part of the chain represented by

```
  O
  ‖
  C
 / \N/
    |
    H
```

is planar, i.e. that there is no free rotation around the CN bond. The chain can then only turn a corner at

and with this condition the α helix immediately follows. Cochran, Crick and Vand (1952) analysed the diffraction by a helical structure, and Cochran and Crick (1952) showed that the α helix explained diffraction by synthetic polypeptides.

Stage 3. 1952

This stage is represented by two papers on 'The external form of the haemoglobin molecule' by Bragg and Perutz (1952 a, b). The first paper dealt with the change in F values when the density of the salt solution in which the protein molecules are bathed was varied. By a well-known optical principle, if the scattering density of the liquid is changed by an amount $\Delta\rho$ the changes in F values are equal to the F values which would be produced by a uniform volume of density $\Delta\rho$ which has the same external shape as the protein molecule. It was concluded that "the width is about 55 Å in the b and c directions and its length about 65 Å or 80 Å in the a direction. Its volume is approximately 116 000 Å³."

In the second paper the shape was deduced from the packing of the molecules, and agreed with the general overall dimensions of the hydrated molecules based on diffraction effects. The results for three types of crystal (figure 5) were

(*a*) either 50 Å × 50 Å × 75 Å or 55 Å × 55 Å × 65 Å

(*b*) 56 Å × 56 Å × 72 Å

(*c*) 54 Å × 54 Å × 69 Å.

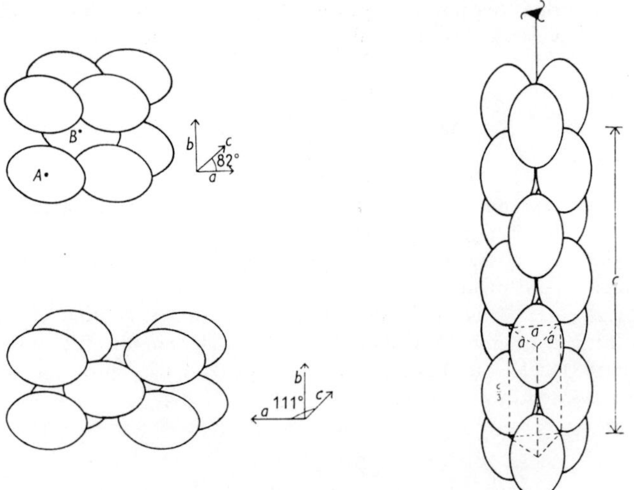

Figure 5. Typical structures illustrating how the spheroidal shape of the molecule was deduced from packing (Bragg and Perutz 1952 b).

Although this determination of the outer form of the molecule is a rather modest result, it is noteworthy as being the first definite quantitative piece of knowledge to be won. Subsequent analysis has shown that in fact the molecule has approximately the shape of a prolate spheroid, the actual dimensions being 50 Å × 55 Å × 64 Å (see also Perutz 1953, Bragg and Pippard 1953).

Stage 4. 1952. The 'transform' methods

The projection of the monoclinic crystal along the *b* axis has a centre of symmetry, and therefore the phases of the diffraction beams in the *b* plane of the reciprocal lattice are + or −. If the signs of all these spots are known, a projection of the molecule on the *b* plane can be formed. The next step was to go as far as possible in determining these signs by using a peculiar feature (Huxley and Kendrew 1953, Bragg and Perutz 1952 c, Perutz 1954) of the shrinking and swelling of haemoglobin crystals shown in figure 6(*a*). During this process the *a* axis, and the *b* axis perpendicular to the plane of the paper in figure 6(*c*) remain constant, indicating that the molecules in sheets in the *ab* plane do not alter their

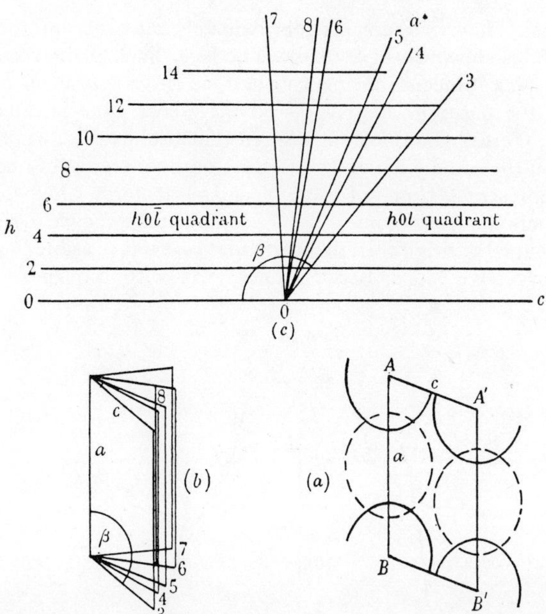

Figure 6. (*a*) Arrangements of molecules in the normal cell of horse methaemoglobin; (*b*) swelling and shrinkage stages; (*c*) relation of transform to stages (Bragg and Perutz 1952 c).

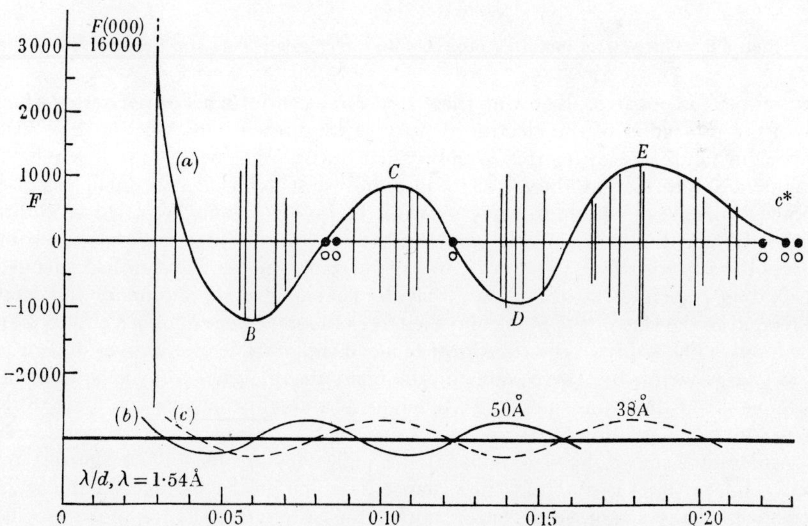

Figure 7. (*a*) *F* values of 00*l* reflections; (*b*) minimal fringe length for a molecule 50 Å in width; (*c*) the same for a molecule 38 Å in width (Bragg and Perutz 1952 c).

relative positions. The *c* axis remains approximately constant, and the main change is in the angle β, as shown in figure 6(*b*). The layer lines of the reciprocal net are shown in figure 6(*c*). Since *a* remains constant, all spots appear on the same set of layer lines, but the position of the spots on these layer lines is different for each shrinkage stage. Perutz laboriously measured the absolute *F* values for each stage. When plotted on the same diagram their values outline a series of nodes and loops, because they represent sections of the molecular transform which passes through a zero value when changing from + to −. For instance figure 7 shows the layer line passing through the origin. In this particular case it is possible to give + and − signs to the successive loops, because one starts with the knowledge that the

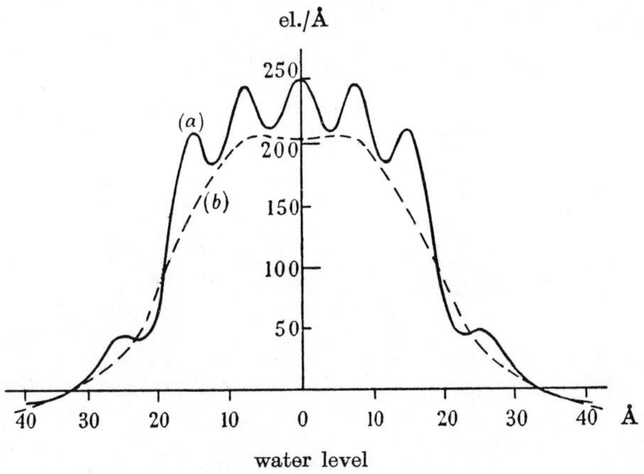

Figure 8. The protein molecule projected on the c^* axis (Bragg and Perutz 1952 c).

central peak is positive. Knowing these signs, one can form a Fourier series which gives the projection of the electron density of the protein molecule on the *c* axis, shown in figure 8. Again this is only worth mentioning because it is a reliable fragment of information, though so meagre, and we snatched at such small successes to keep ourselves in heart to carry on with the investigation. We tried to outline the nodes and the loops for the whole of the reciprocal lattice network. In some places the run was clear, in others it was not certain whether the sign had changed. A guiding principle was the feature that the general scale of the nodes and loops is related to the size of the molecule; the larger the molecule the more crowded are the loops. The study of the transform reduced the possible alternatives of sign by a very large factor, but there were still too many uncertainties to make any further advance along these lines possible. It might be thought that one could relate the signs on one layer line to those on the next by looking for correspondences. Consideration shows, however, that if the molecules are in contact the distance between layer lines is precisely the distance in which on the average the molecular transform changes sign, so defeating any attempt at relation. If the molecules had been isolated from each other by large regions of uniformly dense liquid, interpretation would have been straightforward.

Figure 9, which is taken from the 30th Guthrie lecture, which I gave to the Physical Society in 1952 (Bragg 1952), shows how far we had been able to go along these lines. I am indebted to Perutz for figure 10 which shows the complete

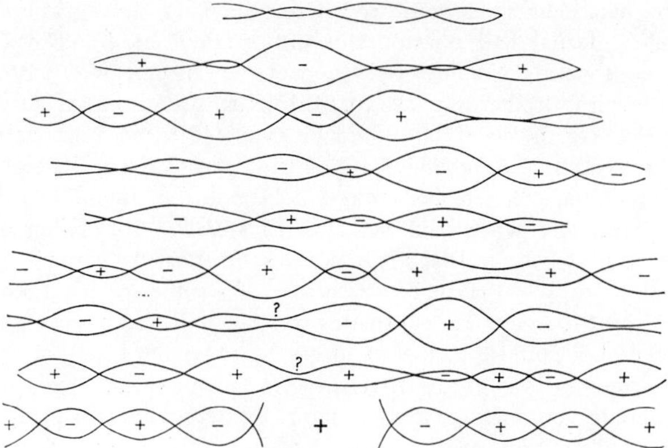

Figure 9. Nodes and loops on layer lines 0–8. The signs of the layers other than the zero layer are conjectural (Bragg 1952).

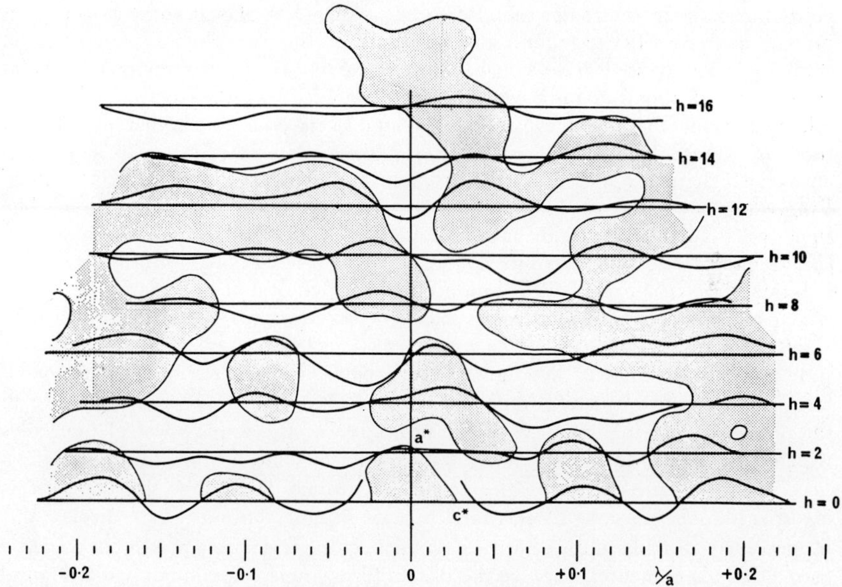

Figure 10. The 'nodes and loops' of figure 9 compared with the complete transform calculated from Perutz's solution of haemoglobin.

molecular transform, with positive areas hatched and negative areas plain. This figure is of course based on the full solution of the haemoglobin structure which came much later; it is interesting to compare the two figures.

Stage 5. Sign determination by the isomorphous replacement method

This paper (Green, Ingram and Perutz 1954) describes Perutz's achievement which marked the turning point in the success of the venture. There was nothing original in the idea that signs would be determined if a heavy atom attachment could be made. Bernal had pointed this out in 1939, in his Royal Institution Discourse. The absolute F values for the protein molecule were known to be of the order of a few hundred at most, so that the contribution made by the diffraction by a heavy atom (e.g. mercury 80) could be expected to be appreciable if one or more such atoms could be attached. Perutz's triumphs were (*a*) the technical one of finding a group containing a heavy atom which could be attached to the molecule at a definite place, and which did not alter in any way the arrangement of the molecules in the unit cell, and (*b*) his expertness in measuring the strength of the spots on the photograph so that he could estimate to a sufficient accuracy the changes in F produced by the heavy atom. In this last his skill was at that time probably unique. I remember coming to Perutz in great excitement one day because I had heard from Professor Roughton that an American worker had succeeded in attaching a mercury complex to haemoglobin in stoichiometric proportions, only to have Perutz tell me very coldly that *he* had given this information to Professor Roughton! The observation which gave the impetus to Perutz's experiments was Rigg's report in 1952 that human haemoglobin combined with two molecules of *para*-chloromercuribenzoate, the 'P.C.M.B.' which has played so large a part in protein analysis. Perutz found the positions of the two mercury atoms by a 'difference Patterson'. The sign of the F contribution by the mercury atom at each point of the transform was therefore known, and the sign of each loop followed at once because it would be the same as that due to the mercury atom if the spot were enhanced, and opposite if it were reduced. Figure 11 shows the answer which then appeared to the problem over which we had puzzled so long. Everything checked and double-checked perfectly; it was a thrilling time. The signs were further checked by a comparison with imidazole-methaemoglobin (Bragg and Howells 1954, Howells and Perutz 1954). This interesting structure presents some very pretty diffraction problems which cannot be gone into here but which may be recommended as an excellent 'exercise for the student' learning about x-ray diffraction.

The determination of the signs made it possible to construct a projection of the structure of the *b* plane (Bragg and Perutz 1954). The nodes and loops give all the necessary information to yield the projection of the single sheet of molecules which is unaltered during shrinking and expansion. This is shown in figure 12.

The nodes and loops of the transform, which figured so largely in this investigation, only came to the fore because haemoglobin crystals display this property of shrinking and swelling. The final complete analysis of protein made no use of this phenomenon, because the phases for a single crystalline form are found by taking advantage of several types of heavy atom attachment. Nevertheless, I think it is justifiable to say that the study of the transform played a vital role at this stage. It enabled the signs to be deduced with a single heavy-atom attachment. If interference caused the mercury contribution to be near zero at one point in a loop, an appreciable value at another point gave the clue to the sign. Everything checked

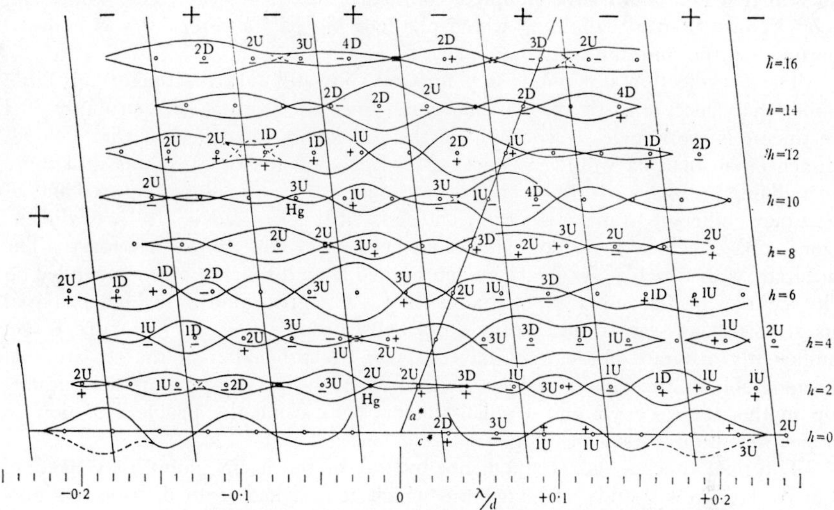

Figure 11. Signs of the nodes and loops solved by adding a heavy atom. The signs + and − refer to the interference fringes produced by mercury atoms on either side of the twofold axis. U and D denote increase or decrease of intensities of diffraction when the heavy atom is added (Green, Ingram and Perutz 1954).

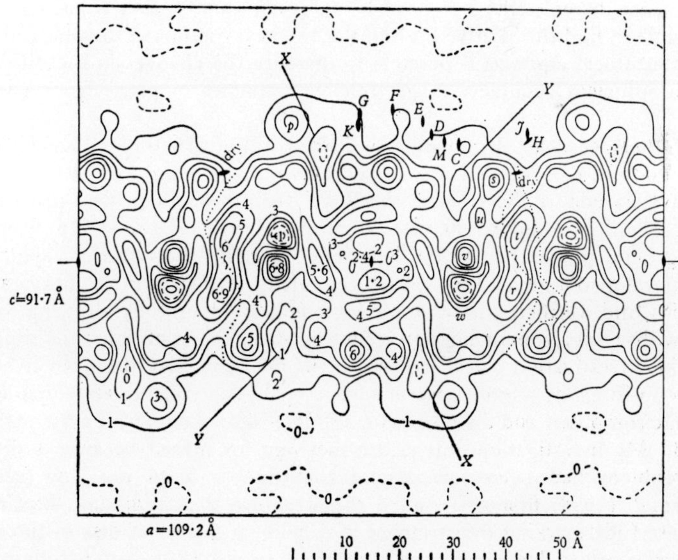

Figure 12. Fourier projection of a row of haemoglobin molecules (Bragg and Perutz 1954).

so well that one could have complete confidence in the answer. The 'nodes and loops' constituted a scaffolding which played a big part although it was knocked away when the building was completed.

The *b* projection was a big step forward, but still told disappointingly little about the structure of the protein molecule, since the features of a structure 50 Å in thickness are hopelessly confused in the projection. It was clear that a three-dimensional analysis would be necessary. Such an analysis presents still more formidable problems. In the *b* projection, signs + or − are alone required and an accuracy sufficient to make the right choice is all that is needed. In three dimensions, phases which may have any value between 0 and 2π are necessary. The accuracy with which phase could be determined for a diffracted beam depended on the accuracy of determination of changes in F. The great question which exercised us at this stage was 'Could heavy atom substitution be used in practice to get sufficiently accurate phases?' I have likened the projection of the structure of haemoglobin on the *b* plane to the establishment of the last camp before the summit; up to this stage Perutz and I collaborated. Now came the problem of how to attack the summit itself.

The final success was attained, not by way of the haemoglobin investigation, but by Kendrew's study of myoglobin which at first had seemed to be less promising. It was quite by chance that Kendrew started his work with myoglobin; a colleague offered him some crystals to investigate. It was at first extremely hard to get crystals of sufficient size until the richness of the source in diving animals was realized. But whereas in haemoglobin it had only been found possible to attach a heavy atom at one site, and this is insufficient for phase determination, Kendrew was able to attach ligands at five distinct sites. Myoglobin also presented a simpler problem because its molecular weight of 17 000 is one-quarter that of haemoglobin. Was it possible to find the relative positions of the heavy atoms in the unit cell with a sufficient accuracy, and was it possible to measure the changes in the diffracted beams with sufficient accuracy, to get reliable estimates of phase from a vector diagram?

It proved to be possible! I remember well the thrill of that time. The collection of the vast body of data needed was shared between the laboratory at Cambridge and the Davy Faraday Laboratory at the Royal Institution. I made a private test of my own. Kendrew supplied me with sets of data for the *hk*0 and 0*kl* projections, for which general phases had to be determined because they have no symmetry centres. I developed a method for getting the relative positions of the heavy atoms (Bragg 1958) and verified that the phases could be found by drawing vector diagrams, with a very convincing agreement between the results for the different ligands. This investigation played no part in the final analysis. Kendrew fixed the heavy atom positions by a more general and powerful analytical treatment aided by the electronic computer, and the phases for all (*hkl*) components were systematically determined. My investigation only had a meaning for myself because it showed that the problem had been solved, and that final success was now certain. Kendrew *et al.* (1958) first determined the structure to a resolution of 6 Å. It showed dense rods marking the stretches of α helix, and the flat disk of the haem group. It was a proud day when he brought the model to show it to me (figure 13, plate II).

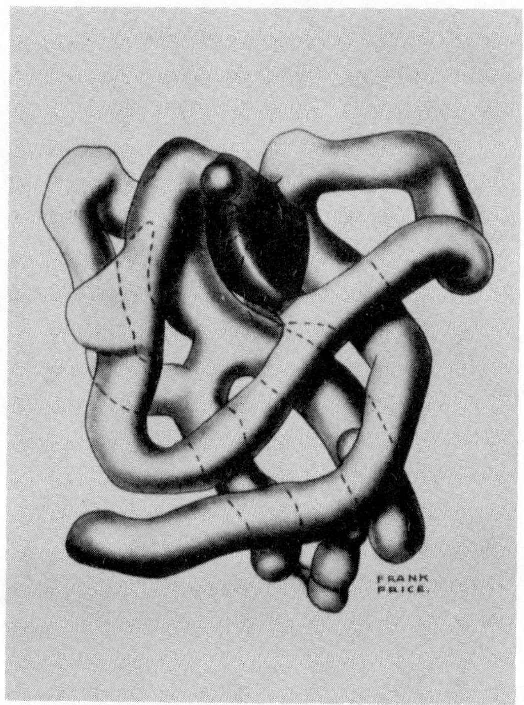

Figure 13. Success at last. Kendrew's analysis of myoglobin to a resolution of 6 Å (Bodo *et al.* 1959).

The story of Kendrew's extension of the analysis of myoglobin to a resolution of 2 Å, and now to 1½ Å, which has led to the fixing of most of the atoms in the molecule, and that of Perutz's elucidation of the structure of the haemoglobin molecule, passes beyond the scope of this paper. It is the story of the work which won them the award of the Nobel Prize which the meeting of the Group commemorated. It has been a wonderful end to twenty-five years of patient investigation with at first very little reward. Fortune relented and smiled at last, for it can be realized now that myoglobin presented a most favourable case. A small molecule, the number of ligand sites, the predominance of the α helices easily recognizable even at 6 Å resolution, and the very characteristic haem group all contributed to success. A measure of the outstanding nature of the achievement is that, although it is five years since the first analysis of myoglobin was made, and the way to success opened up, no other proteins except myoglobin and haemoglobin have as yet been analysed. It will be very interesting to see how long it will be before any other laboratory produces a molecular model of a protein with the wealth of detail now firmly established for myoglobin. My guess, though admittedly a dangerous one, is that it will be between five and ten years before this summit of precision is reached by another party of investigators.

References

Astbury, W. T., 1936, *Nature, Lond.*, **137**, 803.

Bernal, J. D., 1939, *Proc. Roy. Inst. G.B.*, **30**, 541.

Bernal, J. D., and Crowfoot, D., 1934, *Nature, Lond.*, **133**, 794.

Bernal, J. D., Fankuchen, I., and Perutz, M. F., 1938, *Nature, Lond.*, **141**, 523.

Bodo, G., Dintzis, H. M., Kendrew, J. C., and Wyckoff, H. W., 1959, *Proc. Roy. Soc.* A, **253**, 70.

Boyes-Watson, J., Davidson, E., and Perutz, M. F., 1947, *Proc. Roy. Soc.* A, **191**, 83.

Bragg, W. L., 1949, *Proc. Roy. Inst. G.B.*, **34**, 395.

—— 1952, *Proc. Phys. Soc.* B, **65**, 833.

—— 1958, *Acta Cryst.*, **11**, 70.

Bragg, W. L., and Howells, E. R., 1952, *Acta Cryst.*, **5**, 136.

—— 1954, *Acta Cryst.*, **7**, 409.

Bragg, W. L., Howells, E. R., and Perutz, M. F., 1954, *Proc. Roy. Soc.* A, **222**, 33.

Bragg, W. L., Kendrew, J. C., and Perutz, M. F., 1950, *Proc. Roy. Soc.* A, **203**, 321.

Bragg, W. L., and Perutz, M. F., 1952 a, *Acta Cryst.*, **5**, 277.

—— 1952 b, *Acta Cryst.*, **5**, 323.

—— 1952 c, *Proc. Roy. Soc.* A, **213**, 425.

—— 1954, *Proc. Roy. Soc.* A, **225**, 315.

Bragg, W. L., and Pippard, A. B., 1953, *Acta Cryst.*, **6**, 865.

Cochran, W., and Crick, F. H. C., 1952, *Nature, Lond.*, **169**, 234.

Cochran, W., Crick, F. H. C., and Vand, V., 1952, *Acta Cryst.*, **5**, 581.

Green, D. W., Ingram, V. M., and Perutz, M. F., 1954, *Proc. Roy. Soc.* A, **225**, 287.

Howells, E. R., and Perutz, M. F., 1954, *Proc. Roy. Soc.* A, **225**, 308.

Huggins, M. L., 1943, *Chem. Rev.*, **32**, 195.

Huxley, H. E., and Kendrew, J. C., 1953, *Acta Cryst.*, **6**, 76.

Kendrew, J. C., Bodo, G., Dintzis, H. M., Parrish, R. G., Wyckoff, H., and Phillips, D. C., 1958, *Nature, Lond.*, **181**, 662.

Pauling, L., 1940, *J. Amer. Chem. Soc.*, **62**, 2643.

Pauling, L., Corey, R. B., and Branson, H. R., 1951, *Proc. Nat. Acad. Sci., Wash.*, **37**, 205.

Perutz, M. F., 1949, *Proc. Roy. Soc.* A, **195**, 474.

—— 1953, *Acta Cryst.*, **6**, 859.

—— 1954, *Proc. Roy. Soc.* A, **225**, 264.

FIRST STAGES IN THE X-RAY ANALYSIS OF PROTEINS

Sir Lawrence Bragg

ADDENDUM

Note to Final Paragraph

I have been proved to have made far too pessimistic a guess by the students in my own laboratory! The structure of the enzyme lysozyme, the next protein after myoglobin to be fully analysed, was determined by D. Phillips and his colleagues at the Royal Institution in equally great detail not long after I wrote this article, and the structures of a number of proteins have since been established.

Acknowledgment

The researches at the Royal Institution were aided by generous grants from the National Institutes of Health in America.

W. L. Bragg
November 1968

X-RAY CRYSTALLOGRAPHY OF LARGE MOLECULES OF BIOLOGICAL IMPORTANCE

By A. C. T. NORTH

Medical Research Council External Staff, Davy Faraday Research Laboratory, The Royal Institution, London

CONTENTS

Abstract. The electron density within a crystal can be calculated directly if both the amplitudes and phases of the diffracted x-ray beams are known. The multiple isomorphous replacement method has been used successfully for phase determination with several crystalline proteins. Fibrous materials have simpler structures that can often be deduced from the distribution of x-ray intensities without knowledge of phases.

The double helix structure of nucleic acids has led to theories of the genetic code by which inherited characteristics are determined. Several different molecular configurations have been found in fibrous proteins, one of which is also present to a large extent in the crystalline proteins myoglobin and haemoglobin. The very close similarity between these two functionally related proteins is in marked contrast to their unexpectedly complex configurations. Preliminary information has been obtained for two other crystalline proteins and also for several types of virus, which have been found to consist of many identical subunits of as yet undetermined structure.

§ 1. INTRODUCTION

JUST over fifty years ago Laue, Friedrich and Knipping first found that x-rays were diffracted on passing through a crystal and W. L. Bragg showed how the x-ray diffraction patterns could be interpreted so as to reveal the atomic arrangement within the crystal. When the early development of x-ray analysis was discussed by Robertson (1937) in a previous edition of the *Reports on Progress in Physics* twenty-six years ago it was becoming apparent, as a result of the work of Astbury and Bernal, that it might eventually be possible to determine the atomic structures of substances of living origin. These hopes are now being fulfilled, and in this report it is proposed to describe x-ray crystallographic analyses of the structures of proteins, nucleic acids and viruses. It will first be necessary to summarize some of the theory of the x-ray diffraction method.

§ 2. PRINCIPLES OF CRYSTAL STRUCTURE ANALYSIS

2.1. *The Crystal as a Diffraction Grating*

The essential feature of a crystal is that it consists of a basic unit of structure, the unit cell, repeated regularly in a three-dimensional array, the crystal lattice. Each unit cell may contain one or more chemical units (usually molecules).

A crystal acts as a three-dimensional diffraction grating with respect to x-rays, each diffraction spectrum being identified by three indices, h, k, l. W. L. Bragg (1913) showed that each spectrum could be thought of as arising from reflection of the incident beam by a particular set of planes within the crystal. The indices h, k, l indicate the orientation of the planes with respect to the unit cell axes, and the separation d of adjacent planes in the set is related to the equal glancing angles θ that the incident and reflected beams make with the planes, by the Bragg equation

$$n\lambda = 2d \sin \theta \tag{1}$$

in which n is an integer and λ the wavelength of the radiation.

2.2. *Relationships between Electron Density and X-ray Intensity*

When the crystal axes have been so oriented with respect to the incident x-ray beam that the Bragg law is satisfied, the ray reflected from an atom in one unit cell of the crystal is in phase with the rays reflected by the corresponding atom in every other unit cell of the crystal. On the other hand, the ray reflected by one atom will not usually be in phase with the ray reflected by a different atom within the same unit cell, and the intensity of the reflection will depend upon the extent to which the contributions of all the atoms in the unit cell reinforce each other. The phase difference between the ray reflected by an atom at the origin of the unit cell axes and that reflected by an atom whose coordinates, expressed as fractions of the unit cell edges, are x, y, z is $2\pi(hx+ky+lz)$. If f_j is the scattering power of the jth atom, the sum of the contributions from all the atoms to the reflection with indices h, k, l is given by

$$\mathbf{F}_{hkl} = \sum_{j=1}^{n} f_j \exp\left[2\pi i(hx_j + ky_j + lz_j)\right] \tag{2}$$

where n is the number of atoms in the unit cell. $\mathbf{F}_{hkl}$, known as the structure factor of the reflection, is a complex quantity, thus representing both the amplitude and phase of the reflected beam. Its modulus F_{hkl} is known as the structure amplitude, and the intensity of the reflection is given by F_{hkl}^2. (The observed intensity is related to F_{hkl}^2 by geometrical factors depending on the experimental conditions.)

It may be seen that if the unit cell has a centre of symmetry at its origin, i.e. for every atom at x, y, z there is a similar atom at $-x$, $-y$, $-z$, equation (2) becomes

$$\mathbf{F}_{hkl} = \sum_{j=1}^{n} f_j\{\exp[2\pi i(hx_j + ky_j + lz_j)] + \exp[-2\pi i(hx_j + ky_j + lz_j)]\}$$

$$= 2\sum_{j=1}^{n} f_j \cos[2\pi(hx_j + ky_j + lz_j)]. \tag{3}$$

Thus $\mathbf{F}$ is now real, its phase being restricted to 0 or π, i.e. $\mathbf{F} = \pm F$. The summation now includes one atom of each pair.

The quantity f_j, the atomic scattering factor, depends upon the number of electrons belonging to the atom, since it is the electrons which scatter x-rays. As the electron cloud of an atom has finite size, f_j is a function of θ, because as θ increases there is a progressive increase in the phase difference between rays scattered by different parts of the electron cloud. f_j is normally calculated with reference to an atom at rest. The effect of thermal motion at temperatures above absolute zero is to increase the size of the electron cloud. This may be allowed for by multiplying f_j by a temperature factor, a function of exponential form.

Instead of thinking in terms of discrete atoms, one may consider a function ρ_{xyz} representing the electron density at the point with fractional coordinates x, y, z. Then,

$$\mathbf{F}_{hkl} = V\iiint \rho_{xyz} \exp[2\pi i(hx + ky + lz)]\, dx\, dy\, dz, \tag{4}$$

the integration being taken over the unit cell volume, V.

If, as is most often the case, the unit cell contains several groups of atoms or molecules related by symmetry, equations such as (2), (3), (4) can be reduced to simpler forms by taking the summation or integration over the asymmetric unit of structure, i.e. the smallest unit which cannot be further resolved into smaller units related by symmetry.

One of the final stages of a structure analysis is to show that the diffraction pattern calculated in this way agrees sufficiently closely with the observed one. In a few cases, such as very simple structures, compounds which bear a strong resemblance to known compounds or compounds whose structures are closely limited by stereochemical considerations of bonding and packing, it is possible to proceed entirely by trial and error methods, the tentative structure being modified until a configuration is found whose diffraction pattern is in satisfactory agreement with the observed pattern.

However, in the majority of cases, there are too many parameters to be determined for the simple trial and error method to be practicable, although the advent of very high speed electronic computers might revive interest in it as a valid approach. What is required is a way of deriving the structure from the diffraction pattern, rather than vice versa and W. H. Bragg (1915) was the first to point out that, since the electron density in a crystal varies continuously and periodically in three dimensions, it is possible to express it as a three-dimensional Fourier series. Thus,

$$\rho_{xyz} = \sum_p \sum_q \sum_r \mathbf{A}_{pqr} \exp\left[2\pi i(px+qy+rz)\right] \tag{5}$$

where the coefficients $\mathbf{A}_{pqr}$ are complex quantities. If expression (5) is used to substitute for ρ in (4),

$$\mathbf{F}_{hkl} = V\int_x\int_y\int_z\left\{\sum_p\sum_q\sum_r \mathbf{A}_{pqr}\exp\left[2\pi i(px+qy+rz)\right]\right\} \times \exp\left[2\pi i(hx+ky+lz)\right] dx\,dy\,dz. \tag{6}$$

The only term in the summation whose product with the second exponential term does not vanish on integration is that for which $p = -h$, $q = -k$, $r = -l$. Thus

$$\mathbf{F}_{hkl} = V\int_x\int_y\int_z \mathbf{A}_{pqr}\,dx\,dy\,dz = V\mathbf{A}_{pqr}.$$

Hence the equation (5) becomes

$$\rho_{xyz} = \frac{1}{V}\sum_h\sum_k\sum_l \mathbf{F}_{hkl}\exp\left[-2\pi i(hx+ky+lz)\right] \tag{7}$$

and, therefore, the electron density at any point within the crystal can be derived from a Fourier series, the coefficients of whose terms are the structure factors of the X-ray diffraction spectra.

However, the direct application of equation (7) requires knowledge of both the magnitude and phase of each $\mathbf{F}_{hkl}$. Whatever method is used to measure the X-ray reflections only determines intensity, i.e. F_{hkl}^2, and all information relating to the phases of reflections is lost. The problem of supplying the missing information is crucial and the application of X-ray crystallography to structures of increasing complexity has depended upon the development of increasingly powerful ways of overcoming the phase problem; some of the methods used for this will be discussed in §2.3 and §2.4; they fall broadly into three categories: (i) those in which trial structures are deduced from the F values, together with the use of stereo-chemical data to rule out inadmissible structures, (ii) the isomorphous replacement method in which the phases are deduced directly by comparison of the diffraction patterns of very closely related crystals, (iii) the so-called 'direct methods' (see, e.g., Lipson and Cochran 1953) which arise from mathematical properties of the Fourier synthesis together with physical properties of the electron-density distribution. Thus, for instance, the electron density ρ must everywhere be a positive quantity on physical grounds; this does not follow automatically from the form of equation (7) but implies some restraint on the phases of the $\mathbf{F}$'s or the relationships between them. Further, the electron-density distribution in a unit cell that contains a fairly small number of atoms of widely differing atomic number is very non-uniform and it is possible to make deductions concerning probable phase relationships. These methods fall off in power as the number of atoms in the structure increases and if the atoms have generally similar atomic numbers; they have not so far proved useful in the determination of the structures of large molecules of biological origin and, therefore, they will not be discussed further here.

2.2.1. *Projected views of crystal structure.*

The quantity

$$\int_{z=0}^{z=c} \rho_{xyz}\, dz$$

represents the projection of the electron density along the z axis. If the right-hand side of equation (7) is integrated with respect to z, all terms become zero except those for which $l = 0$, i.e.

$$\rho_{xy} = \frac{1}{A} \sum_h \sum_k \mathbf{F}_{hk0} \exp[-2\pi i(hx+ky)] \tag{8}$$

where A is the area of the ab plane. Thus in order to calculate the electron density of a projection of the structure, only the data for a two-dimensional cross section of the X-ray pattern are required. The calculation involves many fewer terms and it is frequently the case that projections of the structure are centro-symmetric even when the structure as a whole is not, resulting in further simplification. Quite often when the packing of molecules in the unit cell is favourable the structure can be deduced entirely from projection data, although three-dimensional methods, which are potentially more accurate, are usually used nowadays in the later stages of crystal analysis.

2.2.2. *Resolution of the Fourier image.*

The summations in equation (7) should ideally be taken over all values of the indices from $-\infty$ to $+\infty$. In fact there are limits to the observable range. Firstly, the smallest value of d that can satisfy the Bragg equation $n\lambda = 2d \sin\theta$ is $\lambda/2$; obviously the shorter the wavelength, the more reflections are observable. Secondly, the effect of disorder in a crystal is to cause a fall-off in the intensity of the diffraction pattern compared with what would be expected from a perfectly ordered crystal. The amount of this diminution increases with $\sin\theta$ so that there is a limit beyond which reflections are too weak to be recorded. All crystals are disordered to some extent but the disorder can often be reduced by cooling the crystal to reduce thermal motion. Thirdly, the atomic scattering factors themselves fall off as $\sin\theta$ increases. Whichever factor is limiting in any particular case, only a finite number of terms will be used for the summation and frequently an arbitrary cut-off will be applied depending on the detail required in the map. The results of series termination are very similar to those in the corresponding situation in optical microscopy. If d is the spacing corresponding to the highest indices included, it will not be possible to resolve in the map features separated by less than about $d/2$. Further, if the series is terminated while coefficients are still large, prominent features in the map may be surrounded by diffraction ripples with confusing effect. Such ripples may be reduced by artificially damping down the coefficients of the highest terms, but at the expense of further reduction in resolution. However, positions of features can be derived to within much closer limits than the theoretical resolution provided that assumptions can be made about their shapes.

2.3. *Proceeding without Phases*

2.3.1. *Refinement of trial structures.*

Once an approximate solution to a structure has been obtained, there are several methods that can be used for refining it. In the Fourier refinement method, the current values of the atomic parameters are used to calculate structure factors. The *phases* of these *calculated* **F**'s are then used with the *observed magnitudes* to derive an electron-density map which should suggest a closer approximation to the true structure. The cycle of operations is repeated until satisfactory agreement between calculated and observed F's has been achieved.

A second procedure, widely used now that electronic computers are readily available, is based on the method of least squares (Hughes 1941); the crystal parameters, principally atomic coordinates and temperature factors, are varied so as to minimize the discrepancy between the calculated and observed F's. An advantage of the method is that the observations can be weighted according to their relative reliability.

X-ray analysis of simple crystal structures has led to detailed knowledge of the geometrical properties of the various types of atomic bond and to the observation that similar chemical environments are usually reflected in similar geometrical relationships. These stereo-chemical principles are of the greatest help in the determination of new crystal structures, particularly in the case of the large molecules of biological origin which are generally built up from small basic units.

2.3.2. *The Patterson function.*

Before the various refinement methods can be used it is of course necessary to postulate a trial structure. This stage of the work usually involves the use of the Patterson function (Patterson 1934). Let us consider the function defined by

$$P_{uvw} = V\int_x\int_y\int_z \rho_{xyz}\,\rho_{x+u,y+v,z+w}\,dx\,dy\,dz. \tag{9}$$

We may substitute for the ρ's by use of equation (7),

$$P_{uvw} = \frac{1}{V}\int_x\int_y\int_z\left\{\sum_h\sum_k\sum_l\sum_{h'}\sum_{k'}\sum_{l'} \mathbf{F}_{hkl}\,\mathbf{F}_{h'k'l'}\exp\left[-2\pi i(hx+ky+lz)\right]\right.$$
$$\left.\times\exp\left[-2\pi i(h'x+k'y+l'z)\right]\exp\left[-2\pi i(h'u+k'v+l'w)\right]\right\}dx\,dy\,dz. \tag{10}$$

Again we find that, multiplying the series together term by term and then integrating over the volume of the unit cell, all the products disappear except those for which $h=-h'$, $k=-k'$ and $l=-l'$. Thus

$$P_{uvw} = \frac{1}{V}\sum_h\sum_k\sum_l \mathbf{F}_{hkl}\,\mathbf{F}_{\bar{h}\bar{k}\bar{l}}\exp\left[2\pi i(hu+kv+lw)\right]. \tag{11}$$

$\mathbf{F}_{hkl}$ and $\mathbf{F}_{\bar{h}\bar{k}\bar{l}}$† are complex conjugates, their product being F_{hkl}^2, a scalar quantity.

Thus, it is possible to generate the function P_{uvw} from the intensities alone, without the phases being required. What does the function P represent? The

† The crystallographic convention $\bar{h}\bar{k}\bar{l}$ is used to denote indices $-h$, $-k$, $-l$.

product within the integration in equation (9) has appreciable values only when both the ρ's have appreciable values simultaneously. Thus every pair of points of finite electron density separated by coordinates u, v, w contributes to the value of P at u, v, w. P is therefore a map, each peak on which arises from a vector between two regions of appreciable electron density or from several such vectors superimposed. Figure 1 shows a set of atoms and the corresponding Patterson map. With

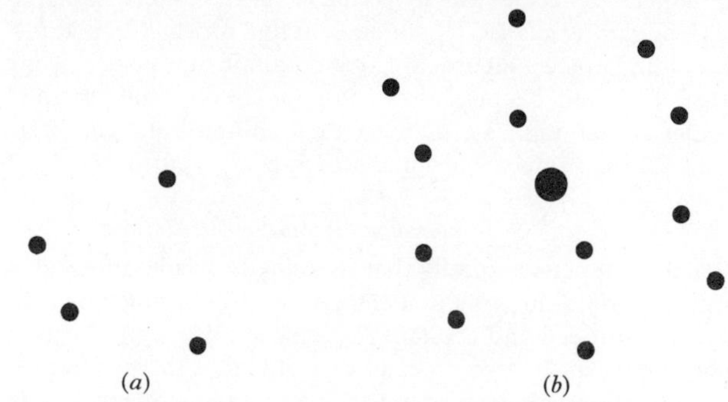

Figure 1. The array of atoms in (*a*) would give rise to the Patterson map (*b*); the large circle lies at the origin of the Patterson map.

the Patterson method, instead of deducing the relative phases of the x-ray reflections, we have to deduce the relative positions of the interatomic vectors in order to assemble them into a consistent set. Again, of course, principles of stereo-chemistry are an important guide in selecting a plausible model. In such a simple case as figure 1 shows it would be easy to derive the actual configuration of atoms from the Patterson map. In more complicated cases the interpretation of the map is more difficult; where there are n atoms in the structure, there are n^2 peaks in the Patterson map of which n coalesce at the origin. If the structure consists of a large number of atoms of similar atomic number, the problem is not very tractable. It is much easier if there are a few atoms of much greater atomic number than the rest. The densities of the peaks depend upon the products of the densities of the two regions related by the vector. Thus vectors respectively between two carbon atoms, between two mercury atoms and between one carbon and one mercury atom will ideally give rise to peaks whose heights are in the ratio 36:6400:480. Hence, if a structure contains a small number of relatively heavy atoms, it is usually possible to deduce their positions from the highest peaks of the Patterson map.

2.3.3. *The heavy atom method.*

If the heavy atoms can be located from the Patterson map, the phases of their contributions to the x-ray pattern can be calculated and used with the observed amplitudes to give the first electron-density Fourier map. This approach is more powerful than might appear at first sight. Even when the scattering power of the heavy atoms is less than that of the rest of the atoms added together, for most reflections the contributions of the various light atoms are largely out of phase with each other, so that the dominating contributions are those of the heavy atoms. For most reflections, therefore, it is a reasonable first approximation to take the phase of the heavy atom contribution as the phase of the total. This general approach, first applied to phthalocyanine (Robertson and Woodward 1940), has been very widely used. Even when a substance does not naturally contain a suitable heavy atom it is often possible to prepare, say, an iodide or a heavy metal derivative.

The necessity for the heavy atom contributions to dominate a large proportion of the reflections sets a limit to the size of structure which can be solved, and, at present, the largest molecule which has been tackled successfully in this way is vitamin B_{12} (Hodgkin *et al.* 1957), which contains ninety-three atoms (apart from hydrogen) including one cobalt atom. Cobalt, atomic number 27, is not particularly heavy, so that it should be possible to use the heavy atom method for slightly larger molecules containing, say, mercury or uranium, but the method is not very likely to be useful for protein molecules which contain a thousand or more atoms.

2.4. *The Isomorphous Replacement Method*

It occasionally happens naturally that two closely related molecules, for instance the potassium and rubidium salts of a compound, have isomorphous crystal forms; that is to say, the unit cell and crystal symmetry are precisely the same, so that the only difference between the two types of crystal is that the positions occupied by a rubidium ion in one crystal are occupied by a potassium ion in the other. The result is that the relative intensities of the X-ray reflections from the two crystals will be different, but not their positions. By comparing the two sets of intensity data, it is possible to deduce the location of the atom which is different in the two crystals, then to calculate the contribution which that atom would make to each reflection and finally to deduce the phase of the resultant contribution of the remaining atoms. In the case of several globular proteins it has been found possible in certain circumstances to combine the native protein with a small molecule containing a fairly heavy atom such as mercury and to crystallize the resulting complex in a form isomorphous with the native protein crystals (Green, Ingram and Perutz 1954). In such cases the heavy atom compound probably occupies space which is filled in the native crystal by liquid of crystallization. The atoms other than the heavy one in the compound usually have roughly the same electron density as do the atoms of the liquid of crystallization, so that, to a first approximation, the difference between the protein derivative and the native protein is due solely to the presence or absence of a single heavy atom. Distinction must be made between the heavy atom method and the isomorphous replacement method; in the heavy atom method use is made of one crystal form containing an atom sufficiently heavy to dominate the X-ray scattering. In isomorphous replacement more than one crystal is studied; the additional atom (or atoms) need not dominate the scattering but it is still desirable for it to be as heavy as possible so that the intensity differences are large compared with errors of measurement. In discussing the method it is convenient to refer to the effect of the 'heavy atom', it being understood that, strictly speaking, isomorphous replacement is being used.

Let $\mathbf{F}_P$ be the structure factor of a reflection from the native protein crystal, $\mathbf{F}_{PH}$ that for the corresponding reflection from the crystal containing the additional heavy atom, and $\mathbf{f}$ the contribution of the heavy atom alone. We can write the vector equation

$$\mathbf{F}_{PH} = \mathbf{F}_P + \mathbf{f}. \tag{12}$$

The first task in solving the crystal structure is to deduce the position of the heavy atom; this can more readily be accomplished when the crystal is centro-symmetric or if there are one or more centro-symmetric projections. If this is the case we may express $\mathbf{F}_{PH}$ as $\pm F_{PH}$ and so forth, and obtain

$$\mathbf{f} = \pm F_{PH} \pm F_P. \tag{13}$$

For most reflections $\mathbf{f}$ will not be so great that $\mathbf{F}_{PH}$ and $\mathbf{F}_P$ have different signs and we can calculate a Patterson synthesis using $(F_{PH} - F_P)^2$ as coefficients. Such a Patterson map will contain only peaks referring to vectors between two heavy atoms so that the heavy atom coordinates can be readily deduced. There may be spurious detail in the map if several reflections have in fact changed sign, but if the map is difficult to interpret it is probable either that the two crystals are not strictly isomorphous or that the heavy atom compound has become attached at several independent sites on the protein molecule, neither of which are favourable circumstances. When a crystal does not have sufficient centro-symmetric projections for all the heavy atom coordinates to be obtained in the above manner, the problem is a little more difficult but it can usually be solved by rather similar methods.

When the heavy atoms have been located roughly their parameters can be refined by the classical methods. The effective atomic number of the heavy atom is an additional parameter involved, as it is frequently the case that the heavy atom compound is not attached to every molecule in the substituted crystal, but, say, to 70% of them distributed randomly throughout the crystal; the effect of this is as if each site were occupied by an atom of 70% of the true weight. A further parameter involved is the relative scales of the two sets of intensity data from the native protein and the heavy atom derivative respectively. In a typical case the effect of the additional heavy atom is to raise the average intensity by about 5%. It is difficult to measure the absolute scale of the intensity data to within that degree of precision so that it is necessary to deduce the ratio of the relative scales from the heavy atom content and then to refine its value. The ratio of the scales and the effective weight of the heavy atom are of course closely correlated.

With precise parameters for the heavy atoms, their contribution to each reflection can be calculated. In the case of centro-symmetric reflections (i.e. those whose phases are restricted to 0 or π by crystal symmetry) it is straightforward to deduce the sign of the protein contribution; if the intensity of the protein reflection has been increased by the addition of heavy atom, the protein structure factor must have the same sign as the heavy atom contribution, and if it has been decreased, the opposite sign. The few cases for which the heavy atom has caused a change of sign are usually obvious because for them f is more nearly equal to $F_P + F_{PH}$ than to $|F_P - F_{PH}|$. However, there will be a certain proportion of the reflections for which the heavy atom contribution is weak so that the difference between F_P and F_{PH} is less than the experimental error in their values; for these, it is not possible to deduce signs with any certainty. In practice, in order to obtain signs for anything like all the reflections, it is necessary to have a second isomorphous compound in which the heavy atom occupies a different position in the unit cell so that there are very few reflections to which one or other of the heavy atoms does not make a significant contribution.

When the phase of a reflection is not restricted to 0 or π it is necessary to draw the vector triangle corresponding to equation (12), figure 2(*a*), in order to determine it. In practice we only know the lengths of the vectors $\mathbf{F}_{\mathrm{P}}$ and $\mathbf{F}_{\mathrm{PH}}$, not their directions (i.e. their phases), but we know both the length and direction of $\mathbf{f}$. We can attempt to reconstruct the complete diagram by drawing the vector $\mathbf{f}$ (figure 2(*b*)) and constructing a circle of radius F_{P} from one end and another of radius F_{PH} from the other (Harker 1956). The circles intersect at the point Q revealing the triangle of figure 2(*a*). Unfortunately they also intersect at R giving a second possible triangle. The two solutions of this diagram are equally valid. When only a single

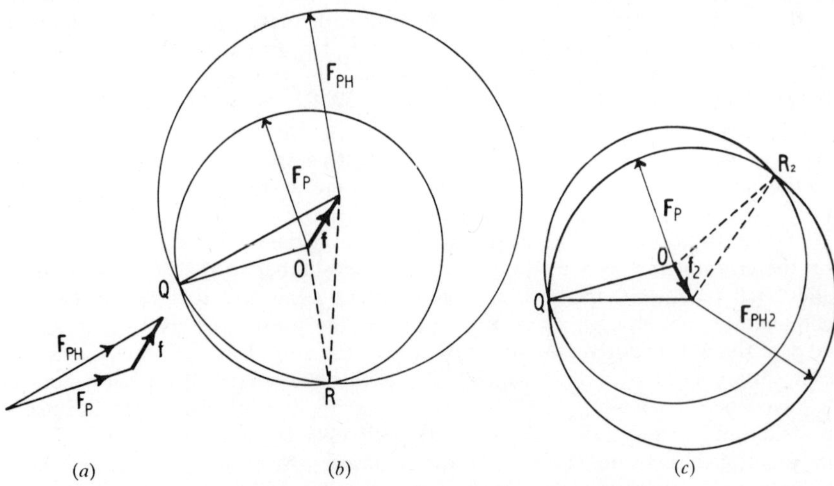

Figure 2. (*a*) Vectorial addition of the protein contribution $\mathbf{F}_{\mathrm{P}}$ and the heavy-atom contribution $\mathbf{f}$ gives $\mathbf{F}_{\mathrm{PH}}$, the structure factor of the protein derivative. (*b*) Circles, of radius $\mathbf{F}_{\mathrm{P}}$ and $\mathbf{F}_{\mathrm{PH}}$ respectively, drawn from the ends of the known heavy-atom vector $\mathbf{f}$ intersect to give the correct solution (solid lines) and a second possible solution (broken lines). (*c*) Data for a second heavy-atom compound also give two solutions; the solution common to (*b*) and (*c*) is the correct one.

isomorphous derivative is available the resultant of the vectors OQ and OR may be used, but there will be considerable background 'noise' in the electron-density map. The ambiguity may be resolved if a second isomorphous derivative is available with the heavy atom in a different site. A second diagram can now be drawn (figure 2(*c*)) again giving two possible solutions; one of these solutions is the same as one of the solutions of the first diagram, so the phase of the protein structure factor can now be deduced unequivocally. Thus, formally, two isomorphous derivatives are required for the solution of non-centro-symmetric reflections. Nevertheless, as with the centro-symmetric reflections, it is desirable to have more than the minimum number in order to cover cases in which the contribution from one or other heavy atom is small. In any case, because of experimental error, the ideal of two perfectly coincident solutions is rarely realized so that the more compounds available the better. In practice, all the vectors and circles are drawn on the same diagram and figure 3 shows typical examples from the structure determination of lysozyme (Blake *et al.* 1962). Whereas figure 3(*a*) approaches the ideal, the two possible solutions of figure 3(*c*) are about 180° apart. Figure 3(*b*) is an intermediate case in which, although there is imperfect agreement between the three compounds, the phase can be found to within 30° or so. Instead of actually drawing circles the problem can be formulated for solution by an electronic computer (Cullis *et al.* 1961, Dickerson, Kendrew and Strandberg 1961). Taking account of the errors of measurement the computer can calculate the appropriate

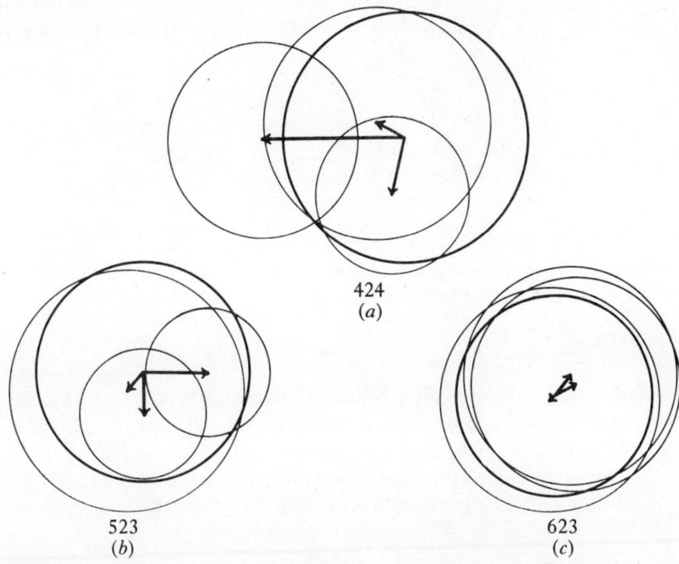

Figure 3. Phase diagrams for three reflections of lysozyme; the native protein circle is heavy. Phase determination is good for the 424 reflection, moderate for 523, poor for 623.

phase angle together with a 'figure of merit' (Blow and Crick 1959) that indicates the reliability of the determination. It has been shown that the most error-free electron-density map can be derived by weighting the Fourier coefficients by the figure of merit for the corresponding phase.

2.4.1. *Use of anomalous scattering.*

There is a second possible method of distinguishing between the two solutions of figure 2(*b*) which makes use of the phenomenon of anomalous scattering. In general, the X-ray wave suffers a phase change of π when it is scattered by an atom. When the wavelength of the X-ray beam is slightly less than that of an absorption edge of the scattering atom, anomalous scattering causes an additional small advance in the phase of the scattered ray. It is possible to select a wavelength such that the additional heavy atoms in the substituted crystal give rise to appreciable anomalous scattering whereas the unchanged atoms do not. This is essentially the case for a protein molecule containing a heavy atom of mercury with the commonly used copper Kα radiation. Consider the vector diagrams for the *hkl* and $\bar{h}\bar{k}\bar{l}$ reflections from such a crystal; equation (2) shows that the structure factors for such a pair of reflections have equal amplitudes but phases with opposite signs. Figure 4 illustrates the $\mathbf{F}_P$, $\mathbf{F}_{PH}$ and $\mathbf{f}$ vectors.

The effect of anomalous scattering is to advance the phase of each of the $\mathbf{f}$ vectors, i.e. to rotate them anti-clockwise to the dotted position. The resultant $\mathbf{F}_{PH}$ vectors are now of different lengths for the two reflections. If the measured difference between the intensities of the pair of reflections is significant, it indicates whether the heavy atom component is in advance or in retard of the native protein component thereby resolving the ambiguity in the solution of the phase diagram. The

Figure 4. The effect of anomalous scattering is to rotate the heavy-atom vectors anti-clockwise from the solid to the dotted positions. Without anomalous scattering, $\mathbf{F}_{PH}$ for (*a*) the *hkl* and (*b*) the $\bar{h}\bar{k}\bar{l}$ reflections would be the same in magnitude; anomalous scattering makes them differ.

intensity differences due to anomalous dispersion are on average much smaller than the differences due to isomorphous replacement by a heavy atom; on the other hand, measurement of anomalous dispersion differences involves comparing intensities of two reflections from the same crystal, thus avoiding the difficulties of scaling together the two sets of data from an isomorphous pair.

2.5. *X-ray Fibre Diagrams*

So far we have been discussing x-ray diffraction from conventional crystals. Some molecules, of very great biological importance, which consist of long chains, form fibres. In most fibres each molecular chain has a straight axis (it may be in the form of a tightly wound helix with a straight axis, like a curtain wire). Within the fibre all the molecular axes are parallel, or nearly so. Occasionally, fibres are formed by the end-to-end aggregation of rather more globular units, like strings of sausages. In either case the complete fibre consists of a number of crystallites, miniature fibres each of which still contains a large number of molecular chains. The crystallites within a fibre have their long axes parallel to each other but are randomly rotated about these axes. The result is that the x-ray diagram from a fibre looks rather like that from a crystal which has been rotated continuously during the exposure to x-rays. X-ray reflections produced at different orientations of the individual crystallite are superimposed.

Crystallographically, there are two distinct types of fibre; in crystalline fibres, molecules within each crystallite are arranged in precise orientations and positions with respect to each other. It is possible to define a unit cell just as in a normal crystal, although a single chemical molecule may run through a large number of unit cells, its backbone configuration repeating exactly in each one. In *para*-crystalline fibres on the other hand, although all the molecular chains within a crystallite are parallel, they are not in precise lateral register, but are displaced randomly up or down. The result is that the x-ray diffraction pattern is no longer confined to discrete spots. Figure 20 (plate V) shows such a pattern; intensity is still confined to layer lines on the pattern since each individual molecular chain has its own regular periodicity. The equatorial (central) layer line alone contains discrete spots because, as we saw earlier, the intensities on a central plane of the pattern arise from the projected density of the structure, and the random displacement of molecules parallel to the fibre axis does not affect the regularity of the projected view along the axis.

With a *para*-crystalline fibre, apart from the equatorial region, there is no way at all of separating out the intensity diffracted by the crystallite at different orientations about its axis. It is possible to derive a type of Patterson function, but otherwise it is necessary to use the simple trial and error method, i.e. to postulate a model structure and then test whether its diffraction pattern resembles the observed one. In view of the paucity of the experimental data there is always a doubt as to whether there are other possible structural models which would agree as well as the postulated one with the observed pattern, but the uncertainty is comparatively small if agreement between observed and calculated pattern is very close and if the model is convincing from the stereo-chemical point of view.

For crystalline fibres once the unit cell has been determined it is possible to resolve and index many of the spots on the pattern, although overlapping may occur, particularly at higher indices. Nevertheless, it is possible to use the conventional method of refinement with observed amplitudes and calculated phases to a certain extent once a structural model has been put forward.

In most fibres the axis of the molecular chain has a helical configuration (a straight axis being a limiting case of a helix) and the general characteristics of the diffraction pattern from a helical structure have been derived (Cochran, Crick and Vand 1952). The basic dimensions of the helix, its pitch and the length of a single unit are indicated by prominent features of the diffraction pattern, so that the diffraction pattern reveals the overall geometry of the structure, which closely limits the possible models.

§ 3. APPLICATION OF X-RAY CRYSTALLOGRAPHY TO LARGE MOLECULES OF BIOLOGICAL ORIGIN

3.1. *Introduction*

Proteins and nucleic acids are two types of polymer which are essential to all living organisms. The monomer units of proteins are amino acids and those of nucleic acids, nucleotides. The sequence of nucleotides in a nucleic acid molecule is now taken to constitute the genetic code which passes inherited characteristics from one generation to the next; this genetic code controls the functioning of living cells, determining both the sequence of amino acids in each type of protein and also the types of protein which are made in any type of cell.

Proteins fall into two classes, structural and metabolic. Structural proteins include keratin, which constitutes hair, wool, horn, finger nails; collagen, the protein of tendon and skin which also forms the reinforcing matrix of bones; myosin, one of the proteins found in muscle, which, although structural, is also actively involved in muscular contraction. The other, metabolic, proteins are for the most part enzymes, that is molecules which act as catalysts in promoting the various processes of breakdown and synthesis which are essential to living matter. Examples of such proteins are trypsin and pepsin, digestive enzymes which are responsible for breaking down protein contained in foods so that eventually single amino acids are released and can be used for building the protein molecules needed by the body. Other enzymes break nucleic acids down but many catalyse much simpler reactions.

Although the methods of chemistry can go a long way towards revealing the characteristics of these various kinds of molecules, it is clear from the highly specific nature of the functions of many of them that a knowledge of the actual spatial configuration of the molecules is essential for the complete understanding of their modes of action. In the past ten years or so X-ray crystallography has begun to supply such knowledge.

It is proposed now to consider X-ray diffraction studies of nucleic acids and proteins and also of viruses, the simplest replicating organisms, which contain both nucleic acids and protein in an intimate relationship.

3.2. *Nucleic Acids*

The structural unit of a nucleic acid, a nucleotide, consists of a base, a sugar ring and a phosphate group. Nucleotides are joined together through bonds linking adjacent sugar rings to form a polynucleotide chain. Two types of nucleic acid occur naturally, deoxyribonucleic acid (DNA) and ribonucleic acid (RNA) which differ in containing the sugars deoxyribose and ribose respectively. Four types of base are found in RNA; two are purines, adenine and guanine, and two pyrimidines, uracil and cytosine. In DNA, thymine (5-methyl uracil) occurs instead of uracil. Other bases are found in small quantities but for our purposes they are all closely related to one or other of the common ones.

In higher organisms both DNA and RNA occur; DNA seems to carry the basic genetic code and several types of RNA appear to be concerned in putting the code into effect in protein synthesis and cell metabolism. Since some viruses contain only RNA this too is capable of preserving the code from one generation to the next. Most animal viruses, on the other hand, contain only DNA but they may, in fact, make use of RNA provided by the host cells.

Astbury and Bell (1938) obtained X-ray diffraction patterns from DNA fibres which showed an intense reflection from planes spaced 3·4 Å apart in the direction of the fibre axis; Astbury (1947) suggested that the nucleotide bases might be stacked like a 'pile of pennies'. Later, Riley and Oster (1951) obtained photographs of unoriented samples of much improved DNA preparations, which showed that specimens could exist in either a crystalline or semi-crystalline form, depending upon the moisture content of the surrounding atmosphere. In the same year Wilkins, Gosling and Seeds (1951) obtained well-oriented fibre diagrams from the same material; since then Wilkins and his group at King's College, London, have continued to improve the quality of the x-ray data (figure 5(*a*), plate I) by refined experimental methods and with the aid of better chemical preparations. Franklin and Gosling (1953 a) obtained fibre diagrams of both the crystalline and semi-crystalline forms and showed that they corresponded to two different configurations of the DNA molecule, termed A and B respectively. The B configuration was found to exist in DNA's from various sources including intact cells (Wilkins and Randall 1953), so that the form observed in the fibres was clearly a natural one of biological significance and not an artefact.

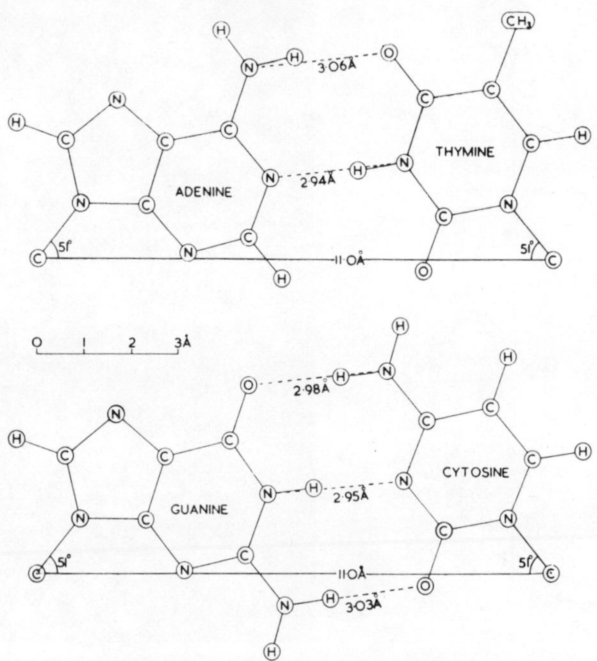

Figure 6. The two Watson–Crick base-pairs, showing their overall geometrical similarity. (After Spencer 1959.)

In the early 1950's various pieces of information began to accumulate; the exact chemical linkages in the polynucleotide chain, about which there had been some uncertainty, were elucidated (Brown and Todd 1952); it was shown that the DNA bases were joined together by hydrogen bonds (Gulland and Jordan 1947); the configuration of an individual nucleoside (nucleotide without the phosphate group) was derived by x-ray diffraction (Furberg 1950); the x-ray pattern to be expected from a helical structure was calculated (Cochran, Crick and Vand 1952); a further result from chemical studies was that, although the proportions of the different bases varied widely with the source of the DNA, the number of adenine bases was always equal to the number of thymine bases and the number of cytosines was equal to the number of guanines (Chargaff 1950), which suggested some kind of pairing (Wyatt and Cohen 1953).

Crick and Watson (1954) then proposed a specific scheme involving hydrogen-bonding of the bases in pairs such that the relative positions of the sugar-phosphate backbones of the two nucleotides so linked were exactly the same for the two possible base-pair arrangements (figure 6). This removed one of the main stumbling blocks in proposing a structural model of DNA, that the structure had to accommodate an

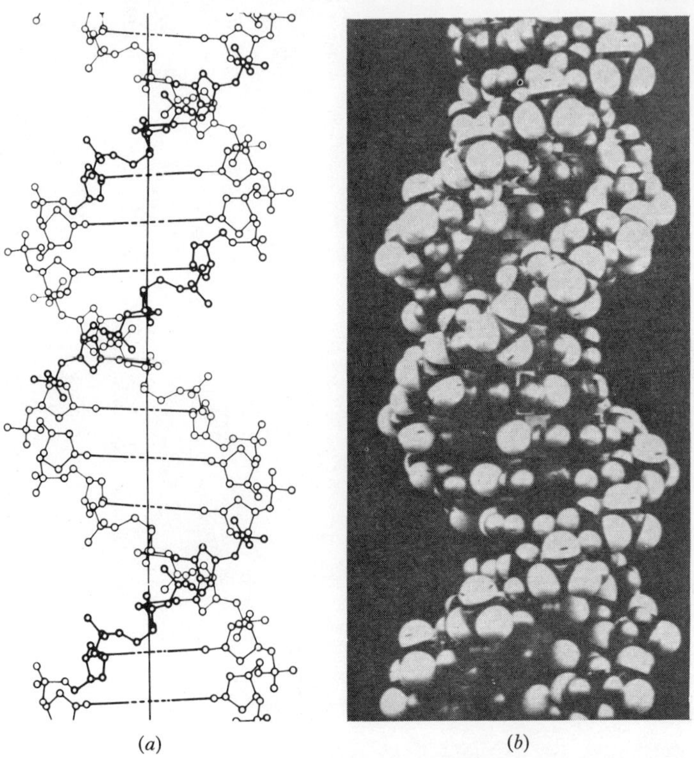

Figure 7. DNA structure B; the two helical chains are linked by hydrogen-bonded base-pairs, represented by the straight lines nearly perpendicular to the helix axis. The five-membered sugar rings and tetrahedral phosphate groups can also be seen. (*a*) shows the interatomic linkages and (*b*) a space-filling model. (By kind permission of Dr. M. H. F. Wilkins.)

irregular sequence of the four bases of different chemical configuration. Crick and Watson put forward a model in which two polynucleotide chains were intertwined in the form of a double helix with each base in one chain pointing inwards and hydrogen-bonded to a base on the other chain. The base-pairs are thus stacked in a pile, as Astbury had suggested, and the two chains, running in opposite directions with respect to the helix axis, form a skeleton into which either base-pair can be introduced at any position. Since the presence of a base, say adenine, in one chain is always associated with a particular 'mate', in this case thymine, at the corresponding position of the other chain, there is a complete complementarity between the sequences of bases along the two chains, and this feature of the structure, which is of the utmost biological significance, will be discussed later.

The Crick and Watson model was found to be broadly compatible with the X-ray fibre diagrams although there were marked discrepancies in detail; it was found that structure A corresponded to a configuration having eleven bases per turn of the helix (Wilkins, Stokes and Wilson 1953, Franklin and Gosling 1953 b), whereas in structure B there were ten bases per turn (Feughelman *et al.* 1955). Wilkins and his group then refined the parameters of the structural models until they found two configurations that were in satisfactory agreement with the X-ray data for forms A and B respectively (figure 7) and that were simply related so that the slight uncoiling from ten to eleven bases per turn when water content was increased could also be accounted for (Langridge *et al.* 1957). The nucleic acid studied in most of the earlier experimental work had been prepared as the sodium salt; later, other metals were used as cations and it was found that the lithium salt could be obtained in a structure B configuration in which the molecular packing was crystalline, instead of *para*-crystalline as in the sodium salt. An advantage in studying this form was that the B configuration had been found to occur in nature whereas A had not, although the crystallinity of A had made it the better form for structural studies. The lithium DNA data have been used for further refinement of the structural model, together with recent information on the stereo-chemistry of the individual nucleotides (Langridge ,Wilson, Hooper, Wilkins and Hamilton 1960, Langridge, Marvin, Seeds, Wilson, Hooper, Wilkins and Hamilton 1960). Since the Crick and Watson scheme was put forward other possible ways of forming hydrogen-bonded base-pairs have been proposed, but the original scheme appears to give the best agreement with the X-ray data and to be stereo-chemically the most satisfactory.

Despite the ambiguities which, in principle, bedevil the interpretation of fibre diagrams, there now seems to be virtually no doubt that the Watson–Crick–Wilkins structure is not only satisfactory but unique.

3.3. *Structure of RNA*

Unlike DNA, most RNA extracts from cells do not exhibit evidence of complementarity in their base compositions. X-ray fibre diagrams obtained from such RNA preparations have been of poor quality compared with DNA. Rich and Davies and their colleagues approached the problem by preparing and studying synthetic polynucleotides, such as polyadenylic acid (Rich, Davies, Crick and Watson 1961), and copolymers of the various nucleotides (Rich 1959, Davies 1960), though without shedding light on the RNA structure. In the past few years, however, it has been found possible to fractionate RNA extracted from cells into several components, one type of which, known as transfer RNA, is found to have base complementarity.

Wilkins and his group (Spencer, Fuller, Wilkins and Brown 1962) have very recently examined specimens of transfer RNA and have obtained greatly improved X-ray diagrams which show clearly that the structure is similar to that of DNA. They have also re-examined the diffraction patterns of other types of RNA and have found them to resemble patterns from poorly ordered DNA specimens. They think, in agreement with Fresco, Alberts and Doty (1960), that those RNA's which do not possess overall base complementarity contain a single chain doubled back on itself with regions distributed statistically throughout its length where localized complementarity is achieved over several bases. In such regions the chain presumably forms Watson–Crick type pairing, and therefore a DNA-like configuration. Mis-matching over a range of one or two bases between two runs of matched bases might result simply in a distortion of the double helix. Mis-matching over longer regions might result in one part of the chain making a loop away from the double helix until correct matching could be resumed. Such a structure would be expected to yield an X-ray diagram similar to that of a very poorly oriented DNA specimen, and the X-ray observations are consistent with this interpretation.

3.4. *Biological Implications of the DNA Structure*

It is difficult to overestimate the significance of the theory of base-pairing, and the proof of its existence in DNA, in the study of living systems. The wide fields of research which have been opened up by this work are mainly outside the scope of this review, but a few of the implications of the results will now be discussed.

The complementary nature of the two chains which make up a DNA double helix immediately suggests a way in which genetic information can be reproduced (Watson and Crick 1953). If the two chains become separated in a medium containing free nucleotides of all four types, each chain forms a template to which the free nucleotides can become attached; individual nucleotides will be preferentially attracted to their appropriate 'mates' and a new complementary chain will be formed by adjacent units linking together. This will happen round each of the chains of the original pair, so that there are now two molecules identical to the original one.

That new double chains are formed from each half of the original double chain has now been demonstrated in a number of cases. Meselson and Stahl (1958) used a heavy isotope of N to grow a generation of DNA with above-average density. They used sensitive density-gradient centrifugation methods to show that the next generation of DNA, grown in the presence of nucleotides containing normal nitrogen, had density intermediate between the normal and the heavy values, so that the double helices must have contained one heavy and one normal chain. The following generation contained equal proportions of normal–normal and normal–heavy.

The form of the DNA structure leads to several possible ways in which genetic mutation can be explained. Slight chemical modifications to one type of base may give it some of the properties of another type, so that a mis-match may be produced. Some chemicals which are known to be mutagens, for example acridine orange, have structural similarities to parts of the DNA molecule; it is thought that the flat acridine orange molecules may become interleaved between adjacent base-pairs, leading to mistakes when replication next takes place.

Accidental changes in the genetic code may result in the production of a modified, possibly inactive, protein. Such a change may have important consequences if it occurs in sperm cells carrying information that will affect the basic inheritance of a new individual; it may also be important if the missing or defective protein molecule is of a type that regulates the balance of the cell metabolism, with the result that cell activity gets out of control. Conditions like cancer are very likely due to such a cause. Occasional mutations of course have beneficial effects, giving rise to systems with new potentialities, and this, linked with the lower viability of strains which have suffered undesirable mutations, has been the basis of evolutionary progress.

The evidence is generally consistent with the theory that the genetic code is expressed in the sequence of the four bases, adenine, guanine, thymine and cytosine, along chains of DNA. If such a code is to determine the sequence of amino acids in a protein molecule, since there are twenty common amino acids, it is apparent that there is not a direct correspondence between the two types of sequence. It is now very probable that each amino acid is selected according to a code of three successive DNA bases (see e.g. Crick, Barnett, Brenner and Watts-Tobin 1961). Such a triplet code could allow for sixty-four (4^3) different amino acids if all combinations were possible. (But a code of two bases per amino acid would only allow sixteen combinations, which would be insufficient.) There are quite wide variations in the base compositions of their DNA's between species which have very similar overall amino acid compositions. This may be because different species use different codes, but it is more likely that, since there appears to be redundancy in the code, some amino acids may be selected by more than one possible triplet. The matter is not yet settled, but within the past year biochemists have taken the first successful steps towards 'cracking' the code by introducing synthetic polynucleotides into systems containing free amino acids and other substances required for protein synthesis. Thus it appears for instance that polyuridylic acid stimulates the synthesis of polyphenylalanine (Nirenberg and Matthaei 1961). Of the additional, rarer, amino acids, some at least are known to be formed by modification of common ones after assembly of the polypeptide chain.

Although there is ample evidence that the DNA contained within the cell nucleus is responsible for the amino acid sequence of proteins, it has been known for some time that the actual site of protein synthesis lies outside the nucleus, in or on particles known as ribosomes which are constructed of RNA and protein. The present theory of protein synthesis (see e.g. Brenner, Jacob and Meselson 1961) suggests that the first step in making a protein molecule is for an RNA molecule to be built up in the nucleus as an exact copy of the relevant part of the DNA. This RNA molecule, known as messenger RNA, then becomes attached to a vacant ribosome and is the actual template by which the protein sequence is determined. There is a further variety of RNA, transfer RNA, one type for each type of amino acid, having presumably at some crucial position in its structure the triplet base sequence corresponding to the amino acid. There is also a set of enzymes, again, one for each type of amino acid, whose function it is to attach the right sort of amino acid to the corresponding sort of transfer RNA molecule. The transfer RNA molecules, with amino acids attached, then assemble themselves in sequence on the messenger RNA molecule on the ribosome. Radioactive labelling methods have been used to show that the amino acids in a protein chain are in fact assembled in order (Dintzis 1961); when the protein chain is completed it is detached from the ribosome which is then available for the production of another protein molecule of the same or another type.

3.5. *Structure of Fibrous Proteins*

The monomer from which proteins are built up is the amino acid, and figure 8 shows some of the commonly occurring ones. As do the nucleotides, all amino acids have a similar backbone part to which different side groups are attached; the side groups have widely differing chemical properties, some being acidic, some basic, some non-polar and some strongly hydrophobic.

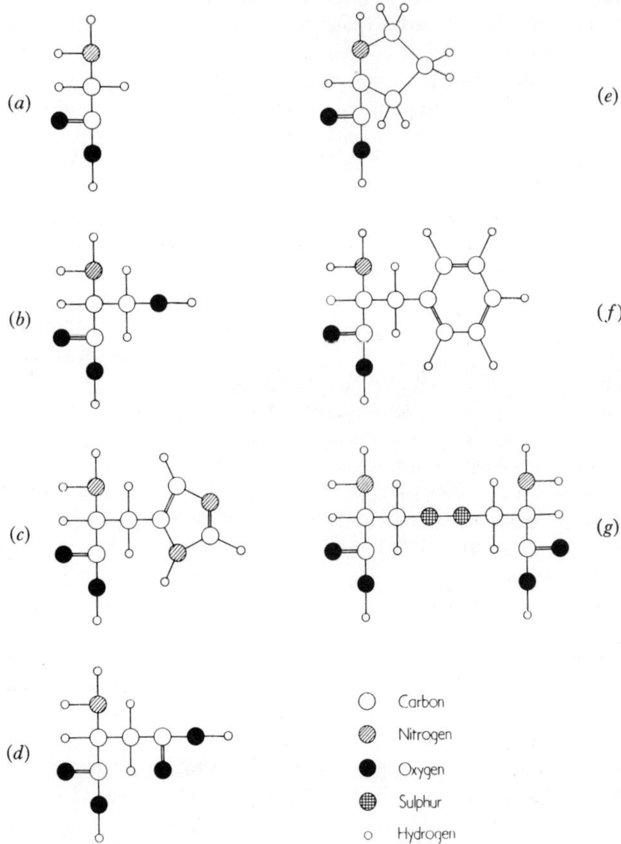

Figure 8. Some of the common amino acids: (*a*) glycine, (*b*) serine, (*c*) histidine, (*d*) aspartic acid, (*e*) proline, (*f*) phenylalanine, (*g*) cystine.

Three of these amino acids have unusual stereo-chemical properties; cystine, which consists of two amino acids linked through a disulphide bridge, and proline and hydroxyproline, in both of which the side chain loops back to the nitrogen atom, forming a ring. The NH_2 group of one amino acid may become joined to the OH group of another amino acid, with the elimination of water to form a peptide bond; such a dimer is called a dipeptide (figure 9) and the process may be repeated indefinitely to form a polypeptide chain. A protein molecule consists of one or more polypeptide chains, often together with a prosthetic group, a group of atoms that is not made up from amino acids and that usually is a chemically important part of the molecule.

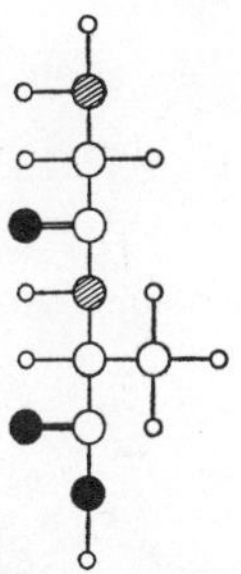

Figure 9. The dipeptide glycyl alanine, formed from the amino acids glycine and alanine.

Fibrous proteins have essentially the simplest structures and until the late 1950's they were the only ones that had been studied successfully by X-ray diffraction. Astbury again was responsible for much of the earlier work and in the early 1930's he classified fibrous proteins into two main groups, the collagen group and the keratin–myosin–epidermin–fibrinogen (k–m–e–f) group (see e.g. Astbury 1940).

3.5.1. *The k–m–e–f group.*

Astbury showed that there were two distinct structural configurations, α (contracted) and β (extended) for members of the k–m–e–f group and that the well-known reversible stretching of wool could be accounted for in terms of a transition from the α to the β form. Wool can be 'set' in either configuration, when it is apparently stabilized by interactions, cystine bridges, hydrogen and polar bonds, between side groups of adjacent polypeptide chains. Some of these linkages are disrupted in the conditions under which the transition takes place and are then remade in a different arrangement; the same phenomenon is made use of in the 'permanent waving' of hair. For the β configuration Astbury proposed a structural model in which the polypeptide chains are nearly fully extended; adjacent chains are linked together to make sheets by hydrogen bonds formed between the NH group of an amino acid residue in one chain and the C=O group of a residue in the next (the term residue is used for the amino acid as it exists in a polypeptide chain, i.e. after the loss of H_2O). The sheets are then packed together with enough space between to accommodate the side chains. Several variations of this basic scheme are possible; within one chain, all the NH groups may point in one direction and all the C=O in the opposite, or they may alternate; adjacent chains may run in the same or opposite directions; adjacent sheets may all be parallel or back-to-back in pairs. With recent values of the basic chain dimensions, it seems probable that one or other of these arrangements occurs in the several forms of silk fibroin and in other members of the k–m–e–f group in the β configuration.

It was obvious that in the α configuration the polypeptide chain must somehow be folded, and Astbury put forward a model which appeared to account for the principal features of the rather poor X-ray fibre diagram then available. In 1951,

Pauling and Corey published the results of an examination of crystal structures of some amino acids and dipeptides, taken together with theoretical considerations, from which they drew certain structural principles (see e.g. Corey and Pauling 1953); the bonds of the amide group

```
H         C
 \       /
  N — C
 /       \\
C         O
```

were always coplanar; precise dimensions could be given to the bond lengths and angles in the amide group; the atoms N—H ... O involved in hydrogen bonds were

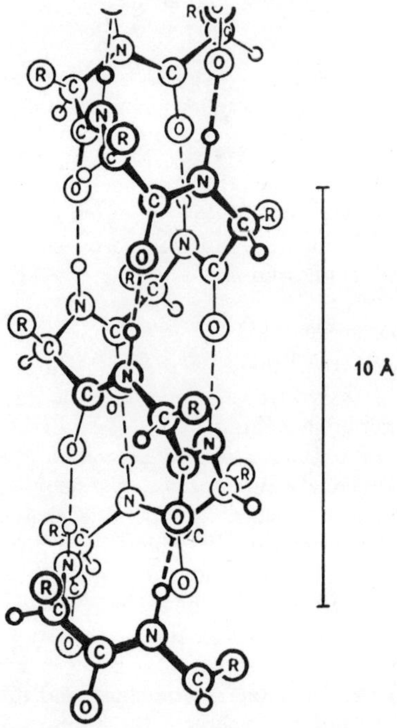

Figure 10. Polypeptide chain in the α-helical configuration. The atoms marked R represent side chains. (From Pauling *et al.* 1951.)

nearly collinear; as many hydrogen bonds as possible were made; certain relative orientations of groups related by single bonds tended to be favoured. Some of the β types of structural model fitted in satisfactorily with these postulates (see e.g. Pauling and Corey 1953). Astbury's α model did not, but Pauling, Corey and Branson (1951) put forward a helical structure in which their principles were obeyed to perfection. In this model, known as the α-helix (figure 10), there are about 3·6 amino acid residues per turn of helix, each residue being hydrogen-bonded to its neighbours in adjacent turns. The helical diffraction theory showed that there was broad agreement between the X-ray pattern expected from the model and the observed diffraction from α proteins; in particular, a reflection corresponding to a spacing of 1·5 Å, the height of one amino acid residue in the structure, was predicted; although it had not been generally observed previously, it was in fact found when the appropriate experimental conditions were used (Perutz 1951).

The difficulty with the interpretation of the X-ray pattern of α proteins in terms of the α-helix is that the very prominent reflection at about 5·3 Å spacing, corresponding to the pitch of the helix, appears to lie on the meridian of the pattern, whereas according to the theory it should not. This has been explained in the

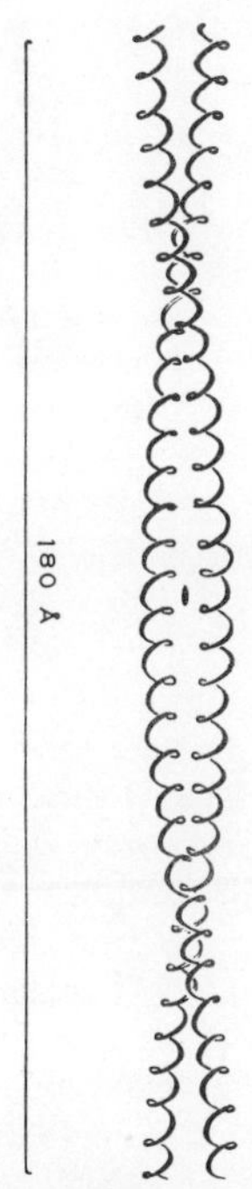

Figure 12. The structure of the paramyosin of molluscan catch-muscle, in which two α-helices are coiled once round each other every 180 Å. (From Cohen and Holmes 1963.)

following way (Crick 1952, 1953): in two turns of the helix, there are 7·2 amino acid residues; since this is just over a whole number, if two adjacent helices pack together so that the side chains on one fit regularly into the spaces between side chains on the other their axes will make a small angle to each other; this form of packing could be maintained indefinitely if the two helices turned round each other, to form a two-stranded rope; each separate strand would then be in the shape of a compound helix or coiled-coil and Crick showed that the reflection corresponding to the pitch of the minor helix would appear on the meridian of the pattern. Very recently, Cohen and Holmes (1963) have obtained beautifully detailed x-ray diagrams (figure 11, plate I) from the paramyosin of molluscan catch-muscle, maintained in a state as near as possible to its environment *in vivo*, which completely support this suggestion. The structural unit in paramyosin can clearly be seen to consist of two supercoiled α-helices, with thirty-five turns of the minor helix and one turn of the major helix in a repeat of 180 Å (figure 12).

Whereas in the case of most of the fibrous proteins, knowledge of the structure is largely an end in itself, the structure of the various muscle proteins and their relationship to each other are of enormous interest in connection with the mechanism of muscular action (Huxley and Hanson 1960). Muscular contraction is thought to result from interleaved sets of myosin and actin fibres sliding past each other, but the chemical mechanism which brings this about is not yet understood.

3.5.2. *Collagen.*

Members of the collagen group of fibrous proteins have a structure which is quite distinct from the α and β forms of the k–m–e–f group. One of the clues to this difference lies in the unusual amino acid composition of collagen; almost exactly one residue in three is glycine, the least bulky amino acid, but about one in four is proline or hydroxyproline. The latter two cannot be fitted into either an α-helix or a normal β sheet, because the ring is rigid and bulky and takes the place of the N—H group which normally participates in hydrogen bonds. Again, Astbury (1933) proposed a structural model for collagen, though neither this nor several other models put forward in the early 1950's were in satisfactory agreement with the x-ray data. As with DNA, several concurrent developments led to the elucidation of the structure. These included: improvements to the x-ray diffraction data, obtained by the use of specimens held under tension (Cowan, North and Randall 1953); application of the newly developed helical diffraction theory to show that collagen too had a helical structure (Cowan, North and Randall 1953, 1954, Ramachandran and Ambady 1954, Cohen and Bear 1953); indications of the orientations of the NH and CO bond directions from infra-red spectroscopy (Ambrose and Elliott 1951, Fraser 1953, Sutherland, Tanner and Wood 1954); the Pauling and Corey stereo-chemical principles (Corey and Pauling 1953); synthesis of the polymer poly-L-proline (Berger, Kurtz and Katchalski 1954), and the determination of its structure (Cowan and McGavin 1955); the discovery that another synthetic polymer, one of the forms of polyglycine, had a similar structure to polyproline (Crick and Rich 1955); studies of the sequences of amino acids in dipeptides and tripeptides extracted from collagen, which showed that proline and hydroxyproline occasionally occurred adjacently within the chains (Schroeder *et al.* 1954, Kroner, Tabroff and McGarr 1955).

In both polyproline and polyglycine, the chains are packed in a hexagonal fashion; each chain consists of a threefold helix, i.e. there are three residues per complete turn; in polyglycine, each residue is hydrogen-bonded to neighbours in adjacent chains, but in polyproline, where no hydrogen bonds can be formed, a similar alignment of chains arises from packing considerations. Each collagen molecule consists of a group of three chains arranged rather like three adjacent chains from polyglycine; instead of their axes being parallel, however, they slowly coil round each other. The total distance before each chain comes back to where

Plate I

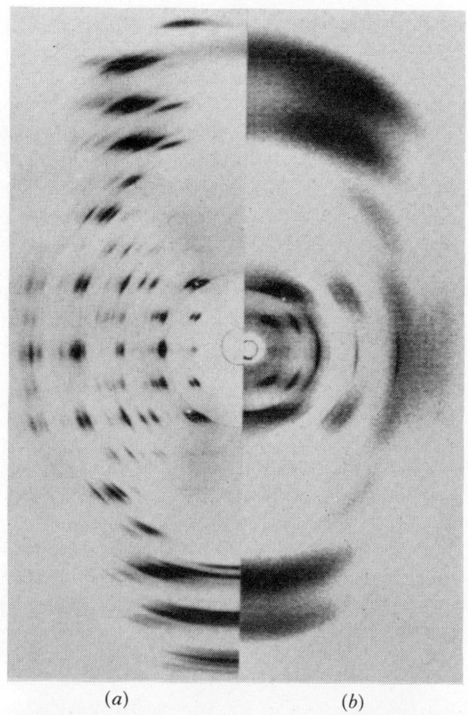

(*a*) (*b*)

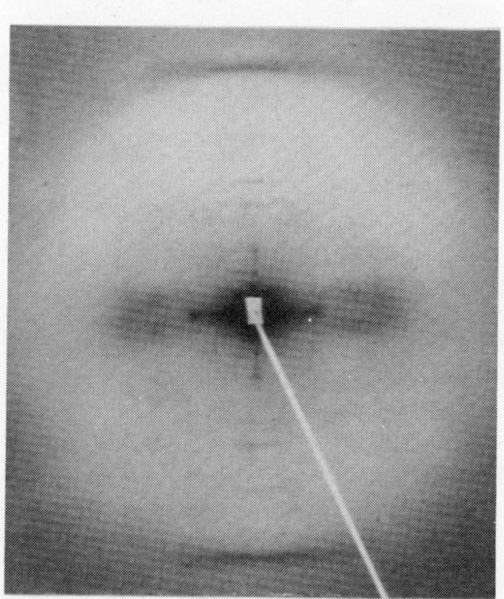

Figure 5. X-ray fibre diagrams of (*a*) DNA in the A configuration, (*b*) crystalline yeast transfer RNA. (From Spencer *et al.* 1963.)

Figure 11. X-ray fibre diagram of an α protein, the paramyosin of molluscan catch-muscle. (From Cohen and Holmes 1963.

PLATE II

Figure 14. 2 Å resolution electron-density map of myoglobin. Density is calculated in a series of sections through the unit cell, and is plotted in the form of contour maps. The dense annular region, below and to the right of centre, represents the projected view along the axis of an α-helical part of the molecule. (By kind permission of Dr. J. C. Kendrew.)

it started from is about 90 Å, containing thirty amino acid residues, in the course of which the chain has made nine 'minor' turns and one 'super' turn around the other chains. One side chain in three of each main chain faces towards the centre of the group of three chains, and there is only room for a glycine residue so that glycine must occur regularly every third residue along each chain; the other side chains face outward, and proline or hydroxyproline may be accommodated in either position. Similarly, one hydrogen bond in three is made regularly and holds the unit of three chains together. The remaining N—H and C═O groups may participate in hydrogen bonds with suitable groups on side chains or with water molecules, but it is not yet clear whether such bonding can form a regular pattern and make an important contribution to the stability of the structure.

This basic model of the collagen chain configuration was arrived at more or less independently by several groups of workers (Ramachandran and Kartha 1955, Rich and Crick 1955, 1961, Cowan, McGavin and North 1955) and appears to be in satisfactory agreement both with the *para*-crystalline type of X-ray diagram, which is still poor compared with that of DNA, and also with present data on amino acid sequences. Collagen fibres show additional order on a much larger scale (Bear 1952, North, Cowan and Randall 1954, Hodge and Schmitt 1960), both longitudinally and transversely which has not yet been explained completely in molecular terms. Although this indicates inhomogeneity in the fine structure it is probable that the configuration deduced from the X-ray data accounts for the greater part of the molecule.

The complementary nature of observations by X-ray diffraction and by electron microscopy has been of great value in the study of collagen, muscle and many other biologically important structures.

3.6. *Structure of Globular Proteins*

In the fibrous proteins, the molecules are arranged parallel to each other, with their chains in an extended form. In the globular proteins, on the other hand, each molecular chain is folded into a compact form, and for X-ray diffraction to be used the protein must be crystallized. Most globular proteins can be crystallized if they can first be obtained in a highly purified form. There are various grounds for supposing that the polypeptide chain is first arranged into a fairly rod-like configuration such as an α-helix, and that this structure is rolled up in some way to give the roughly spheroidal shape generally exhibited by globular proteins. It might, therefore, be hoped that some of the types of structure found in fibrous proteins would occur also in the globular proteins, and this has proved to be the case.

The crystals of globular proteins contain a considerable proportion of mother liquor, usually dilute salt solution, often of the order of 40% of the total weight of crystal. If the crystal is allowed to lose this water by evaporation, the crystal structure collapses. It is, therefore, necessary to mount the crystal in a sealed thin-walled glass capillary that also contains a drop of the crystal mother liquor, during the recording of the X-ray intensities.

At the time of writing, the structures of some four different proteins have been determined to a resolution of 5–6 Å, and one of these, myoglobin, to a resolution of better than 2 Å. From the discussion of the resolution in the Fourier image of a crystal structure given in § 2.2.2, it will be apparent that the higher the resolution aimed at, the greater the number of reflections whose intensities have to be measured; in fact the number of reflections varies roughly with the cube of the reciprocal of the resolution. Thus, some 400 reflections were required for the 6 Å resolution map of myoglobin, 10 000 for the 2 Å map and a further 10 000 to extend the resolution to 1·5 Å (these dimensions are actually the interplanar spacings of the highest-angle reflections included—the actual resolution in the image, as explained in § 2.2.2, should be better than this). The structure of myoglobin, the first of a crystalline protein to be determined in three dimensions, was investigated successively at these three resolutions largely for the reason that it was not clear how well the methods were going to work, and therefore not advisable to go to the lengths of measuring all the data at the beginning. In fact, for each of the proteins investigated subsequently, a low resolution map has been made the first objective as even a 6 Å map may contain useful information about the general nature of the molecular configuration.

Haemoglobin was the first globular protein to be studied intensively, starting about 1937, by Perutz and his colleagues (Bernal, Fankuchen and Perutz 1938). It is the red protein responsible for the colour of blood, whose principal function is to transport oxygen in the blood stream, and it has a molecular weight of 64 500; it contains four polypeptide chains, together with four haem groups (the prosthetic groups that are the site of oxygen combination); in the crystal structure of horse haemoglobin, the molecule consists of two identical halves related by the crystal symmetry, so that it is only necessary to determine the structure of a half molecule of weight 32 200.

Patterson maps were obtained at an early stage and suggested the presence of rod-like features in the molecule; at a later stage unsuccessful attempts were made to explain the X-ray pattern on the basis of parallel lengths of α-helix. By studying a variety of crystal forms of haemoglobins from different animal species and prepared under various conditions, it was found possible to deduce the external shape of the molecule and to show that it had similar configurations in the different crystals. A variety of elegant methods were used to exploit the relationships between the crystal forms to the full (e.g. Bragg and Perutz 1952), but they became of largely academic interest upon the discovery that the isomorphous replacement method could be applied (Green, Ingram and Perutz 1954). Crystals were prepared of compounds in which each molecule of haemoglobin had been combined with two molecules of *para*-chloro-mercuri-benzoate (PCMB) (a benzene derivative containing one mercury atom) or with silver ions. Horse haemoglobin crystals of the form studied contain one centro-symmetric projection, and it was found possible to derive the position of the mercury atom by the difference Patterson method described in § 2.4, and then to determine the signs of a sufficiently large proportion of the reflections for a projection of the protein electron density to be obtained. Unfortunately, this projection proved uninterpretable, partly because the projection was through a considerable 'depth' of molecule and partly because the molecule, as is now known, does not have the underlying regularity that had been anticipated. Nevertheless, it had been shown that the method was feasible, though it would have to be extended to three dimensions.

3.6.1. *Myoglobin.*

Although haemoglobin is not large as protein molecules go, there are many considerably smaller and a number of other investigators were studying smaller molecules in the hope that their crystal structures could be more readily determined. Among these was Kendrew, who was working with myoglobin, which has a molecular weight of 17 000 and consists of a single polypeptide chain and one haem group. Myoglobin is responsible for the storage of oxygen in muscle tissue, a function rather similar to that of haemoglobin, and is possessed in particularly large quantities by diving mammals. Kendrew has studied the myoglobin of the sperm whale. Although he obtained his first isomorphous derivative after Perutz, the problems of obtaining further derivatives and finding their positions in three dimensions in the unit cell were solved sooner for myoglobin so that the 6 Å three-dimensional map of myoglobin was obtained first (Kendrew *et al.* 1958).

Phases for the structure factors of myoglobin were obtained from data for five heavy atom derivatives, each isomorphous with the native protein. Two of these five contained a double substitution consisting of two of the others simultaneously. In principle there is no information derivable from such a compound that could not be obtained from the other two separately but in practice, largely because experimental errors are an important factor in phase determination, the additional information is useful. In each haemoglobin molecule there are four cysteine residues, the sulphydryl groups of which were known to be highly reactive, and the heavy atom groups became covalently linked to them. Myoglobin does not contain sulphydryl groups, and though systematic ways of attaching heavy atoms were tried, there appeared to be little system governing the successful attempts; it appears that the heavy atom compounds went into 'cosy corners' in the protein molecule where the ionic environment was attractive.

The electron density of the salt solution that fills the interstices between the protein molecules is roughly equal to the average electron density of the entire crystal. Regions where the main polypeptide chain is compactly folded would be expected to have density above the average, but where it is loosely folded the density might fall to the average value and regions which are occupied by straggling side chains would have below-average density. Figure 13 shows a model of the regions of the myoglobin molecule of above-average density. The immediately striking impression given by this model is its lack of symmetry or regularity. It is no wonder that attempts to explain such a structure in terms of bundles of parallel chains were unsuccessful. Nevertheless, there are a number of fairly straight rod-like features whose densities and diameters are just what one would expect for α-helices. Apart from one or two places where the density falls to the average value, it is possible to trace above-average density continuously through the model, leaving little doubt that the model shows the course of the polypeptide chain. There is one very dense region at H which must represent the haem group.

One very important point must be borne in mind when it is considered how such a model has been derived. The electron density that is calculated is the density for the whole or part of the unit cell. The position of the protein molecule within the unit cell is not necessarily known, and the first task in interpreting the map is to determine the boundary of a single molecule. If the main chains of two adjacent molecules come very close together, or if fairly dense side chains fill the gap between two molecules, there may be continuous high density running between the molecules; conversely, there may be gaps within one molecule where the density is tenuous. It is unlikely that a molecule will be completely surrounded by salt solution (characterized by uniform, average density) as the packing of molecules in the crystal is probably such as to allow oppositely charged regions of adjacent molecules to come close together. It is, therefore, difficult to determine the molecular boundary from a low-resolution map and sometimes impossible, so that

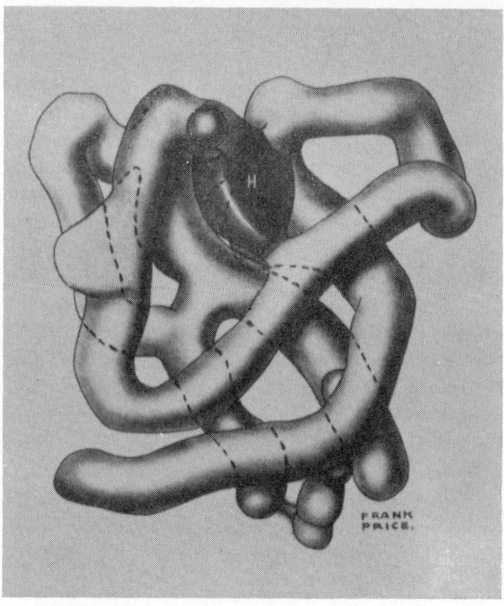

Figure 13. Model of the high-density regions of the sperm-whale myoglobin molecule seen at 6 Å resolution. The dark-coloured disk-shaped region at H is the haem group. The small sphere represents the site of one of the heavy atom groups. (From Bodo *et al.* 1959.)

a model such as that of figure 13 may be incorrect, lacking a piece that should be present and having instead a corresponding piece that should belong to a different molecule. In fact, the higher resolution map of myoglobin shows that Kendrew had been remarkably successful in delineating the molecule and that the model shown is substantially correct.

Following the success of the 6 Å map, it was decided to continue to higher resolution, 2 Å, by means of the same method. It was necessary to determine the coordinates of the heavy atoms rather more accurately and, even then, it was not certain whether the different crystal forms would be sufficiently isomorphous for the phases to be determined well enough. The gradual decrease of average intensity diffracted at higher angles (i.e. smaller spacings) accentuated the problems involved in attaining sufficient accuracy in the intensity data.

The actual task of collecting, measuring and correlating the intensity data was formidable and took a team of about six people well over a year. In order to record the 10 000 reflections from each crystal form it was necessary to take over twenty different photographs, a different crystal being used for each photograph in order to avoid excessive radiation damage. It was very fortunate that the small and relatively slow electronic computers which were available when the 6 Å myoglobin map was being obtained had been superseded by a new generation of larger and faster machines by the time that the 2 Å stage was under way.

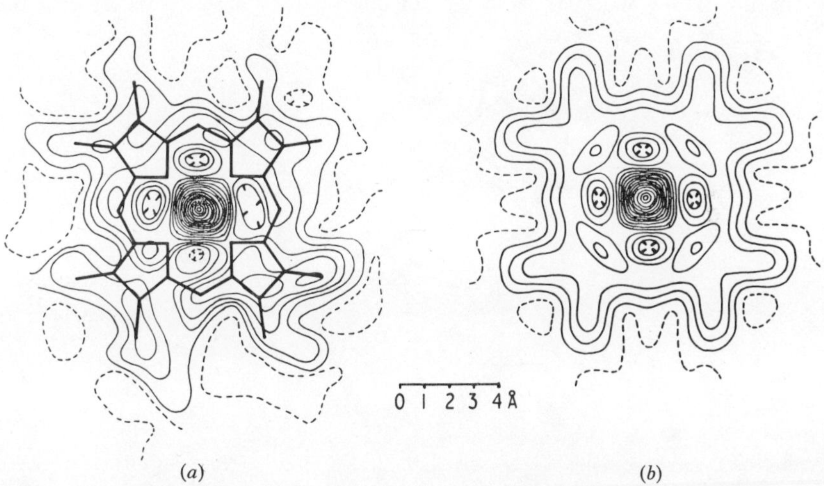

Figure 15. (*a*) Electron density, calculated at 2 Å resolution, in the plane of the haem group, with the atomic arrangement of the group superposed. (*b*) Electron density of an ideal haem group as it would appear at 2 Å resolution. (From Kendrew *et al.* 1960.)

The 2 Å electron-density map was immediately promising (Kendrew *et al.* 1960). The rod-like features of the 6 Å map were now seen to be hollow cylinders (figure 14, plate II), and the variation in electron density along them proved to fit exactly the dimensions of the α-helix. Thus, this configuration of the polypeptide chain, which had been put forward by Pauling and Corey after a study of small peptides and the theory of the chemical bonds involved, had been shown to exist in practice first in fibrous proteins and now in a globular protein. The next striking feature to be apparent was the haem group, consisting of the central iron atom surrounded by a planar arrangement of interlinked five-membered rings. Figure 15(*a*) shows the observed electron density in the plane of the haem group, with a drawing of the atomic arrangement of the group superimposed. Figure 16 shows the way in which the haem group is linked to the polypeptide chain by means of a histidine residue. Although, as was expected, the map does not resolve separate atoms it is possible to determine readily the orientations of groups whose shape is known. The amino acid side chains in general have quite distinctive shapes and it has proved possible to identify a very large proportion of the side chains in good agreement with the chemically determined sequence. The greatest difficulties in doing so occur in regions where the main chain itself straggles round a corner between two lengths of α-helix. The corners are of very great interest, for it is not yet clear what causes the polypeptide chain, after a length of α-helix, to turn a corner and then adopt the α-helix configuration again. There have been suggestions that the protein molecule is built up on a template which determines the geometry as well as the amino acid sequence of the chain. It is difficult to conceive any sort of template on which such a complicated three-dimensional loop as the myoglobin molecule could be laid down. An alternative theory that the

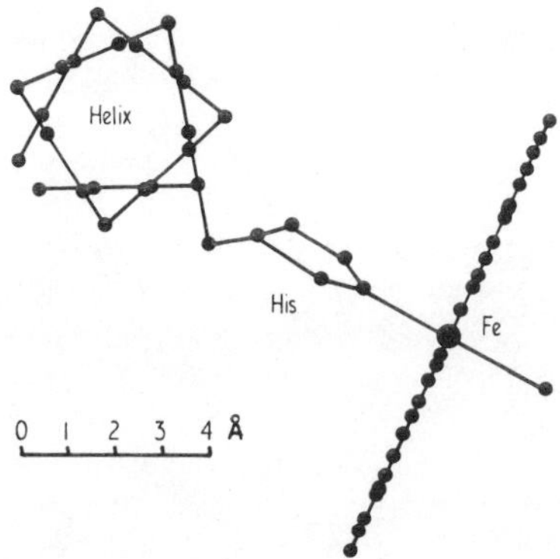

Figure 16. Diagram showing how the haem group, seen in section perpendicular to its plane, is linked to a helical region of the polypeptide chain through a histidine residue. (From Kendrew *et al.* 1960.)

molecule might be made in sections, say of lengths of α-helix, which could then become linked together may be ruled out by the results of Dintzis (1961), who showed that the haemoglobin chains were synthesized by the addition of amino acids in order, working from one end to the other. The remaining possible explanation seems to be that the configuration is determined by the energetically most favourable situations allowed by the amino acid sequence. It was obvious that proline could not be accommodated in an undistorted α-helix and the proline residues in myoglobin do occur at the corners. However, there are more corners than proline residues and it happens that no two corners in myoglobin contain the same sequence of residues. It has been suggested on the basis of spectroscopic data (Blout, de Lozé, Bloom and Fasman 1960) that some sequences of residues may be unfavourable to α-helix formation, for example where bulky or similarly charged side chains occur four residues apart, so that they are close together in adjacent turns of the helix. It seems at present that several more protein structures will have to be determined before a consistent picture will emerge of the relationship between amino acid sequence and chain configuration.

After detailed examination of the 2 Å map of myoglobin it was found possible to give coordinates to about 75% of the atoms (not including hydrogen atoms) (Kendrew *et al.* 1961). A model of the atomic arrangement is shown in figure 17 (plate III). While this examination was proceeding, the intensities of the 10 000 additional reflections involved in extending the resolution to 1·5 Å were being measured for the native protein alone. The phases of these reflections have not been derived from isomorphous replacement, but have been calculated from the contributions of the atoms that were satisfactorily located on the 2 Å map. Refinement of the structure is now proceeding in the conventional way with alternate rounds of structure factor and Fourier synthesis calculations, as progressively more atoms are being located.

3.6.2. *Haemoglobin.*

At the same time as the 2 Å map of myoglobin was obtained, Perutz, Rossmann, Cullis, Muirhead, Will and North (1960) derived the three-dimensional map of haemoglobin at 5·5 Å resolution. As expected, this map showed that each half molecule of haemoglobin contained two polypeptide chains, although it was not anticipated that the configurations of these two chains would be strikingly similar to each other and also to myoglobin. Figure 18 shows a comparison of the three types of chain, and figure 19 shows how the two pairs of chain are arranged roughly tetrahedrally to form the complete molecule of haemoglobin (plates IV, V); it is astonishing that such apparently irregular objects should fit together so neatly. Another point of great biological interest is that the two proteins come from widely differing species (horse and sperm whale).

The amino acid sequences of the haemoglobin chains are largely known and it is possible to correlate the structural differences with the sequence differences (Cullis *et al.* 1962); thus, in the α-chain of haemoglobin, the loop at the top of the model (figure 18(*b*)) is much smaller than in either the β-chain or myoglobin. Comparison of the amino acid sequences shows that several residues are completely omitted from the corresponding region of the α-chain relative to the others.

The fact that there are very many differences between the amino acids at corresponding positions on the three chains, despite which the chains have such similar configurations, does not clarify the relationship between sequence and configuration. Nevertheless, there are a number of crucial places where the same amino acid is found in all three chains. These include a second histidine residue near the iron atom (additional to that shown in figure 16) which is apparently important in the binding of oxygen by myoglobin and haemoglobin; one of the abnormal haemoglobins which has arisen as a result of mutation is unable to bind oxygen and it is found that this histidine residue is replaced by the bulkier tyrosine which blocks access to the iron atom (Gerald and Efron 1961). The various abnormal haemoglobins, which have been recognized in the first place because they are inefficient in their action, have been studied widely by chemical methods in the past few years. Generally they are different from the normal form in just one or two amino acid residues and it is now becoming possible to locate the positions of the abnormal residues on the three-dimensional model. It would be of enormous importance if the change in nucleic acid base sequence responsible for the change in amino acid could be detected.

Each haemoglobin molecule, with four haem groups, is capable of binding four oxygen molecules and it is found that the energy involved in binding (or releasing) each successive molecule becomes progressively less. It therefore requires a much smaller change in oxygen partial pressure in the neighbourhood of a haemoglobin molecule to cause it to lose or gain an oxygen molecule than to cause a myoglobin molecule to do so. Another property of haemoglobin, but not of myoglobin, is that the oxygen affinity is affected by *p*H, and, therefore, by the local concentration of dissolved CO_2. Both these effects are of profound physiological significance and the first appears to be due to interactions between the separate haem groups in the haemoglobin molecule; as these are some considerable distance apart the effect must be transmitted by intervening sections of polypeptide chain; the interaction is destroyed when the sulphydryl groups are blocked by mercurials but we shall have to wait at least for a higher resolution map before the mechanism can be explained.

Why does nature use a molecule of weight 68 000 to carry oxygen around the bloodstream? It is clear that haemoglobin is more efficient than myoglobin for this purpose because of the effects mentioned above. However, at each stage of evolutionary progress when a protein with new potentialities has evolved by modification of an existing one, it does not follow that all the potentialities of the old protein are utilized in the new; it may be the case, therefore, that many of the molecular features in, say, myoglobin are of no use whatsoever, having only been important in a protein ancestor whose function was somewhat different. Thus although we may be able to explain much of the molecular configuration in terms of functional significance we may have to be reconciled to leaving some features unexplained.

The structures of two more proteins, lysozyme and chymotrypsinogen, have recently been determined at 5 or 6 Å resolution. Chymotrypsinogen, molecular weight 25 000, is a precursor of the digestive enzyme chymotrypsin; Kraut, Sieker, High and Freer (1962) have used six isomorphous derivatives to obtain the phases of the reflections. They studied a crystal form that had a comparatively high water content and they had little difficulty in delineating the boundary of a single protein molecule. However, they have been unable to trace the course of the polypeptide chain through the molecule unequivocally at the present resolution. There are two possible reasons for this: the protein contains a much lower proportion of α-helix than myoglobin, so that there are fewer well-defined features contrasting with background density; secondly, there are five cystine residues forming disulphide bridges between different parts of the polypeptide chain. Four sections of chain must diverge from each bridge and it is difficult to determine which connects with which. Thus, whereas myoglobin contains separate prominent rod-like regions, chymotrypsinogen has less compact, interlinking, features and higher resolution will be required for clarification.

Lysozyme, which is contained in many body fluids (e.g. tears and egg-white) is able to hydrolyse constituents of cell walls, so that one of its functions may be to combat infection. It has a molecular weight of 14 000 and has been studied independently by three groups, Blake, Fenn, North, Phillips and Poljak (1962), Stanford, Marsh and Corey (1962) and Dickerson, Reddy, Pinkerton and Steinrauf (1962). The first group have used data, including anomalous scattering measurements, from three isomorphous derivatives in deriving the electron density of a

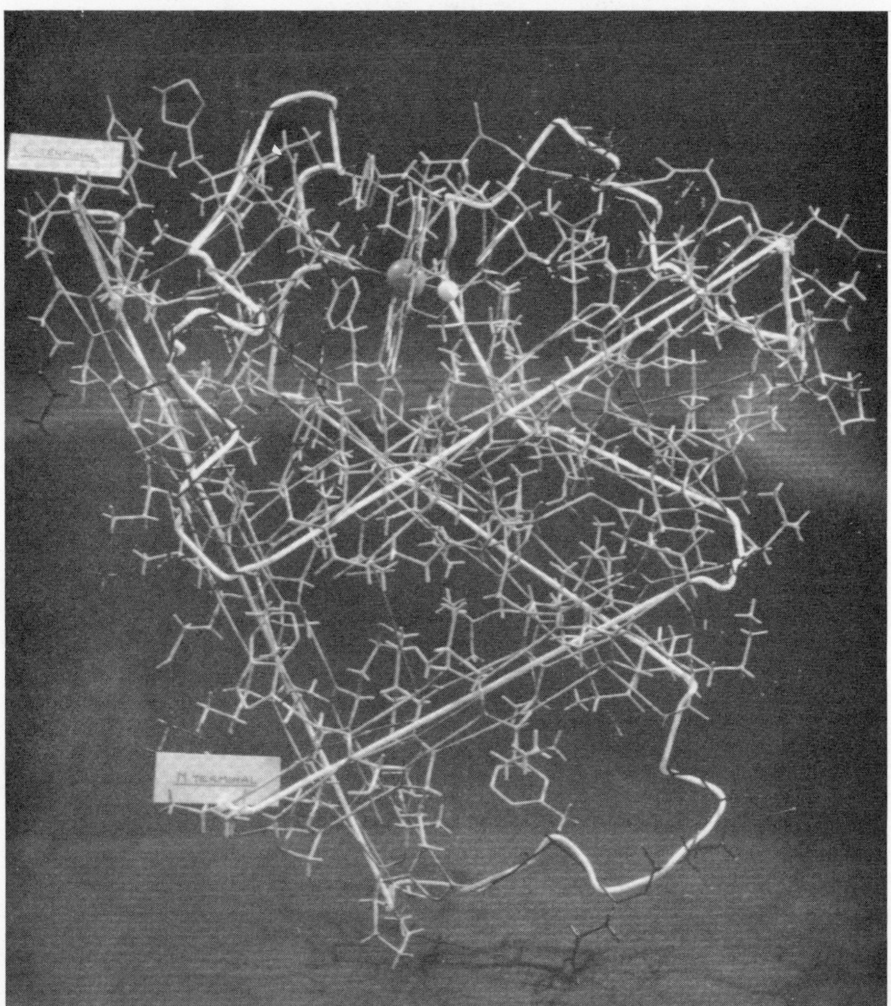

Figure 17. Atomic arrangement in myoglobin derived from the 2 Å electron-density map. The model is painted black in regions where the configuration is uncertain. The string traces the course of the polypeptide chain. The haem group can be seen above the centre. (From Kendrew *et al.* 1961.)

PLATE IV

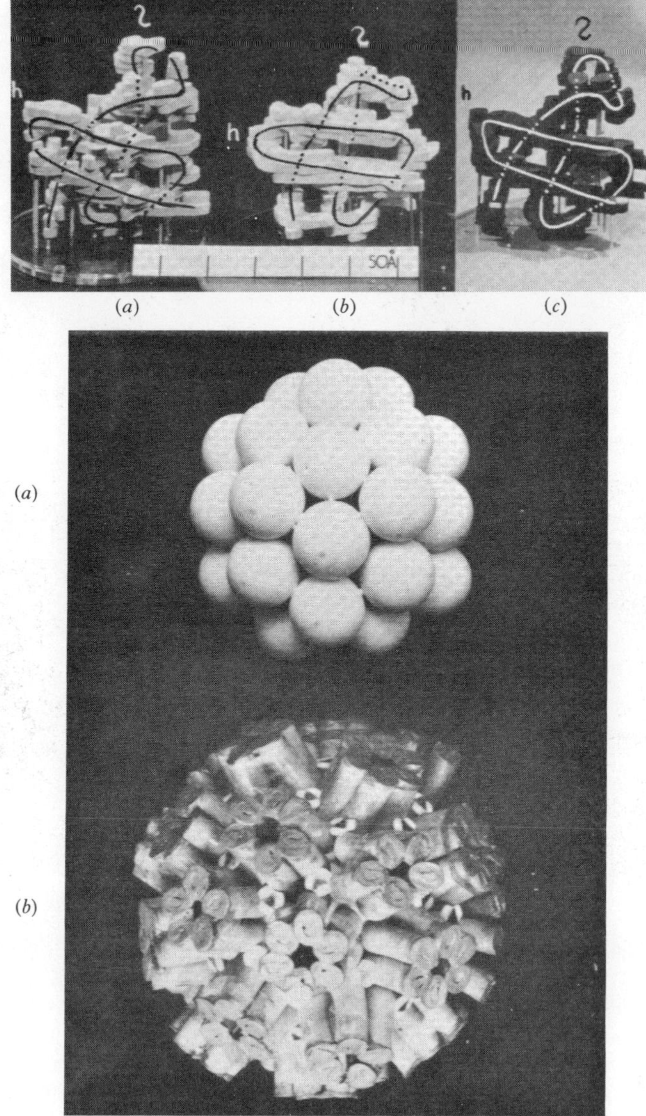

Figure 18. Comparison of high-density regions of (*a*) sperm-whale myoglobin, (*b*) horse haemoglobin α chain, (*c*) horse haemoglobin β chain, at 5·5 Å resolution. The greatest differences seem to be in the uppermost corner and in corner h. (From Perutz *et al*. 1960.)

Figure 22. (*a*) Model illustrating the appearance of a turnip yellow mosaic virus particle in the electron microscope. (*b*) Model, built up from 180 sub-units, which has the general appearance of (*a*) and meets the requirements of the crystal symmetry. (By kind permission of Drs. A. Klug and J. T. Finch.)

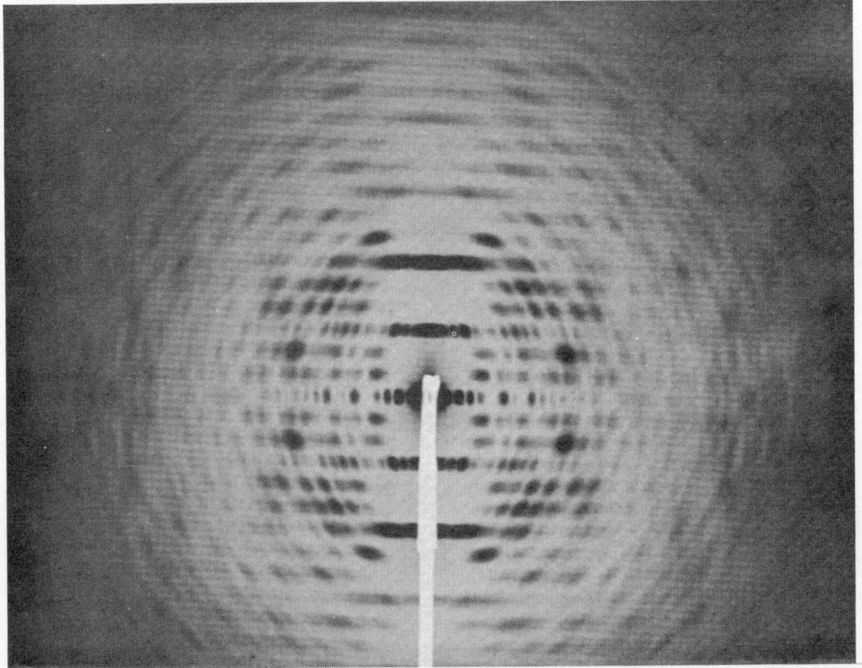

Figure 19. The complete haemoglobin molecule, consisting of two α chains (white) and two β chains (black). (From Perutz *et al.* 1960.)

Figure 20. X-ray diagram from a *para*-crystalline gel of tobacco mosaic virus. (By kind permission of Dr. K. C. Holmes.)

tetragonal form of lysozyme. The second group have studied the same form and have obtained two heavy atom derivatives which are isomorphous with each other, but not with the native protein; they have used the single isomorphous compound method to obtain a map of one of the heavy atom derivatives. The maps of these two groups are as similar as could be expected in view of the slight non-isomorphism and the probable errors in the phase angles. The third group have worked with three isomorphous derivatives of a quite different, triclinic, crystal form of lysozyme. Lysozyme is like chymotrypsinogen in having several (four) disulphide bridges and a fairly low α-helix content, so that it is again difficult to follow the course of the polypeptide chain from the maps. However, it is hoped that detailed comparison of the three maps may assist the interpretation.

Several other proteins are currently being studied, and these include two, insulin and ribonuclease, which have been investigated intensively for a number of years. With neither of these has it yet been found possible to prepare the necessary isomorphous heavy atom derivatives. The low molecular weight, 6000, of insulin and the fact that its amino acid sequence was the first of any protein to be determined make it an obviously attractive object for X-ray study, as is ribonuclease, whose sequence has now also been found and which also has a comparatively low molecular weight, 13 000. It may well be the case that with small proteins there are fewer places in which a heavy atom compound can lodge without affecting the isomorphism of the crystals, so that the apparent advantage of small size from the crystallographic point of view is, in fact, a severe disadvantage.

In view of the difficulties of preparing suitable isomorphous derivatives, it is important to investigate other possible methods of phase determination, and Rossmann and Blow (1962, 1963) have recently been attempting an approach reminiscent of the 'direct' methods referred to in § 2.2. Almost invariably, it is possible to crystallize a protein in several different crystal forms, depending upon the conditions of crystallization. There is therefore, in effect, a redundancy of information describing one molecule. The same applies in cases where the asymmetric unit of structure in a crystal contains more than one molecule, i.e. when there are two or more molecules in the crystal not related by symmetry. It should be possible to exploit this redundancy in order to obtain information about the phases of the reflections in any one form, and Rossmann and Blow are attempting to do this by Fourier methods. An essential requirement for the success of the method is, of course, that the molecular configuration is substantially the same in the crystal forms to be compared.

3.7. *The Structure of Viruses*

Viruses are on the borderline of the living and the inanimate. They are living in that they can reproduce, but they need a host cell in order to do so, and they have a definite and constant structure. Viruses in general contain nucleic acid and protein components, the nucleic acid being the infective part. The protein seems to act mainly as a protective coat but may be enzymatically active in attacking the wall of the host cell. Once inside, the viral nucleic acid takes over from the cell's own nucleic acid and makes use of the cell's supply of raw materials, enzymes and ribosomes, in order to produce more virus particles. When these have been completed they are released leaving behind a dead host cell.

We have already met the fact that proteins may be built up from sub-units in the case of haemoglobin which contains two chains of each of two kinds; it may well be the case that all protein molecules greater than a certain size are made from small units in this way, for there is probably a maximum size that could be dealt with on one ribosome. Further, a smaller amount of genetic information is needed if the sub-units are identical. All viruses seem to be composed of sub-units, and animal and plant viruses fall into two classes, rod-shaped and spherical. Bernal and co-workers (Bernal and Fankuchen 1937, Bernal, Fankuchen and Riley 1938) were the first to obtain x-ray diffraction patterns from viruses of both types. Klug and Caspar (1960) have recently reviewed the subject.

3.7.1. *Tobacco mosaic virus.*

The rod-shaped tobacco mosaic virus (TMV) has been intensively studied. It is possible to prepare gels of TMV, in which the virus particles are aligned with their axes parallel. Such a gel gives an x-ray diffraction pattern (figure 20, plate V) similar to that of a *para*-crystalline fibre, and showing that the sub-units from which

Figure 21. Model of a tobacco mosaic virus particle. The loaf-shaped objects represent the protein sub-units, the beaded filament is the RNA, there being three beads (nucleotides) per protein sub-unit. (From Klug and Caspar 1960.)

the rod is built up are arranged helically. The complete rod, 3000 Å long and about 150 Å in diameter, contains 2130 identical protein sub-units with 49 sub-units to every three turns of a helix of pitch 23 Å (Franklin, Klug and Holmes 1957). It has been found possible to prepare isomorphous derivatives containing lead, mercury or uranium and it is also possible to re-crystallize the protein component alone, without the RNA. Comparison of these structural forms has shown that the RNA is in the form of a single chain helically wound with a radius of 40 Å and a pitch 23 Å, corresponding to that of the protein sub-units. It appears that there are probably three nucleotides of RNA per protein sub-unit. Figure 21 is a diagram of the arrangement of the TMV particle. Two further features are the hole of about 40 Å diameter down the centre of the particle and the grooved outer surface, which permits the particles to pack 150 Å apart in dry gels, although their overall diameters are 180 Å. Both these features have also been observed by electron microscopy. The x-ray studies are also beginning to give some information about the distribution of electron density within the protein sub-units (Franklin and Holmes 1958). The amino acid sequence of the protein has recently been worked out and has shown the position within the chain of the cysteine residue which is the site of the mercury atom, whose radial coordinate had already been determined from the x-ray data. It is possible that this type of approach, in which heavy atoms are used as markers, together with model-building, may play an important part in determining the configuration of the protein chain within the sub-unit. Even though several heavy-atom derivatives are available it will not be possible to calculate the electron-density distribution directly, since the material is *para*-crystalline and the diffraction pattern is, therefore, a rotationally averaged one.

3.7.2. *Spherical viruses.*

It has been found possible to crystallize a number of spherical viruses although no satisfactory isomorphous replacement has yet been attained. Spherical viruses consist of a protein shell surrounding a core of nucleic acid, the protein shell again consisting of a number of identical sub-units arranged in a symmetrical fashion (see Klug and Caspar 1960).

X-ray diagrams have shown that all the viruses so far studied have icosahedral symmetry so that they must contain an integral multiple of sixty sub-units. However, turnip yellow mosaic virus when viewed in the electron microscope (Huxley and Zubay 1960, Nixon and Gibbs 1960) appears to have thirty-two protuberances of roughly equal size on its surface. In order to conform to the x-ray observations (Klug and Finch 1960) each of these protuberances must itself contain symmetry-related sub-units. Figure 22(*a*) shows a model of the virus as it appears in the electron microscope and figure 22(*b*) shows a model containing 180 (3×60) units arranged in clumps of five or six (plate IV), so that the structure would appear to have thirty-two roughly equal lumps and would also satisfy the x-ray symmetry. The actual shapes of the 'sub-units' in the model have no physical significance, for it has not yet been possible to determine the shapes or density distributions of the individual sub-units of any spherical virus nor has it been shown how these geometric sub-units are related to possible chemical sub-units. Some of the other spherical viruses appear to have different external morphologies, to account for which other groupings of the sub-units are required.

§ 4. CONCLUSIONS AND FUTURE PROSPECTS

Although it is difficult to overestimate the importance of the pioneering work of people such as Astbury, Bernal, Hodgkin and Perutz in showing the significance of the x-ray diffraction data given by various substances of biological importance, the full potentialities of the method have only been realized in the past ten years or so.

The most significant single structure from the biological point of view has been DNA because of the fundamental role that the nucleic acids play in controlling the growth and behaviour of living systems. The fibrous proteins have been interesting in their own right and also because they bridge the gap between simple peptides and globular proteins so that the task of interpreting the electron-density map of myoglobin, for example, could be approached with confidence. The structures of the globular proteins are of course interesting from more than one viewpoint. In themselves they will be of enormous help to biochemists in investigating the mechanisms of chemical reactions in living systems; there is also interest from the point of view of genetics in comparing the various proteins within one organism, comparing corresponding proteins in different species separated by various distances on the evolutionary tree, and comparing the different proteins which carry out corresponding functions in different species. The results on viruses hold out hope of knowing more about the way in which nature builds up complex structures from small units and about the structural relationship between protein and nucleic acid in normal cells as well as in viruses. It is in the study of exact spatial arrangement that the X-ray diffraction method excels and this type of information is required in many fields of biological research; for instance, the mechanism of conduction along nerve fibres and the properties of membranes, both of which seem to involve very delicate relationships between lipids, proteins and other cell constituents.

As with most branches of fundamental research, it is to be expected that progress in the application of X-ray diffraction to biological systems may take place in two ways; exploitation of existing methods to study more substances of comparable complexity, and the development of new methods of technique and theory so that systems of still higher complexity can be tackled.

As for the first of these, the prospect of working out the structures of the thousands of enzymes which are known to exist by the methods used up to the present is not an immediately attractive one. However, it is probable that general structural principles will begin to emerge when a few more protein structures have been found and it may be the case that there are comparatively few structural types. Meanwhile, much progress is being made in reducing the labour involved in making the intensity measurements by the use of automatic apparatus and electronic computers. In one of the recently described structure determinations of lysozyme the X-ray intensities were measured on a counter diffractometer which surveyed the pattern systematically and recorded the data on punched paper tape; the tape was then fed directly into the computer which carried out all the further stages of calculation up to the final electron-density map. The main problem to be overcome lies in the preparation of suitable isomorphous derivatives, which is of course a problem in chemistry rather than crystallography. However, there is hope that more systematic ways of preparing isomorphous series of compounds will be found and there is also the prospect of making use of different crystal forms of the same molecule.

Progress in studying more complex structures is largely dependent on advances in chemical methods of separation and purification so that extraneous components can be removed without damaging the essential features of the system being studied. The main requirement on the X-ray side will probably be methods of improving the collimation of the apparatus to allow for the smaller divergence between adjacent spectra from larger unit cells but without appreciably reducing the sensitivity of the intensity measurements. It may also be necessary to take precautions against excessive damage to the specimen by the x-ray beam.

Although there are various problems to be overcome, the results of the past ten years would seem to justify optimism in assessing the prospects of further progress in the study of the structures of biological systems.

ACKNOWLEDGMENTS

Many of the figures in this report have been published previously, and thanks are due to their original authors and publishers for permission to reproduce them.

REFERENCES

AMBROSE, E. J., and ELLIOTT, A., 1951, *Proc. Roy. Soc.* A, **206**, 206.

ASTBURY, W. T., 1933, *Trans. Faraday Soc.*, **29**, 193.

—— 1940, *J. Int. Soc. Leath. Chem.*, **24**, 69.

—— 1947, *Symp. Soc. Exp. Biol.*, **1**, 66.

ASTBURY, W. T., and BELL, F. O., 1938, *Nature, Lond.*, **141**, 747.

BEAR, R. S., 1952, *Advanc. Protein Chem.*, **7**, 69.

BERGER, A., KURTZ, J., and KATCHALSKI, B., 1954, *J. Amer. Chem. Soc.*, **76**, 5552.

BERNAL, J. D., and FANKUCHEN, I., 1937, *Nature, Lond.*, **139**, 923.

BERNAL, J. D., FANKUCHEN, I., and PERUTZ, M. F., 1938, *Nature, Lond.*, **141**, 523.

BERNAL, J. D., FANKUCHEN, I., and RILEY, D. P., 1938, *Nature, Lond.*, **142**, 1075.

BLAKE, C. C. F., FENN, R. H., NORTH, A. C. T., PHILLIPS, D. C., and POLJAK, R. J., 1962, *Nature, Lond.*, **196**, 1173.

BLOUT, E. R., DE LOZÉ, C., BLOOM, S. M., and FASMAN, G. D., 1960, *J. Amer. Chem. Soc.*, **82**, 3787.

BLOW, D. M., and CRICK, F. H. C., 1959, *Acta Cryst.*, **12**, 794.

BODO, G., DINTZIS, H. M., KENDREW, J. C., and WYCKOFF, H. W., 1959, *Proc. Roy. Soc.* A, **253**, 70.

BRAGG, W. H., 1915, *Phil. Trans. Roy. Soc.* A, **215**, 253.

BRAGG, W. L., 1913, *Proc. Camb. Phil. Soc.*, **17**, 43.

BRAGG, W. L., and PERUTZ, M. F., 1952, *Proc. Roy. Soc.* A, **213**, 425.

BRENNER, S., JACOB, F., and MESELSON, M., 1961, *Nature, Lond.*, **190**, 576.

BROWN, D. M., and TODD, A. R., 1952, *J. Chem. Soc.*, 52.

CHARGAFF, E., 1950, *Experientia*, **6**, 201.

COCHRAN, W., CRICK, F. H. C., and VAND, V., 1952, *Acta Cryst.*, **5**, 581.

COHEN, C., and BEAR, R. S., 1953, *J. Amer. Chem. Soc.*, **75**, 2783.

COHEN, C., and HOLMES, K. C., 1963, *J. Mol. Biol.*, in the press.

COREY, R. B., and PAULING, L., 1953, *Proc. Roy. Soc.* B, **141**, 10.

COWAN, P. M., and MCGAVIN, S., 1955, *Nature, Lond.*, **176**, 501.

COWAN, P. M., MCGAVIN, S., and NORTH, A. C. T., 1955, *Nature, Lond.*, **176**, 1062.

COWAN, P. M., NORTH, A. C. T., and RANDALL, J. T., 1953, *The Nature and Structure of Collagen*, Ed. J. T. Randall (London: Butterworth), p. 241.

—— 1955, *Symp. Soc. Exp. Biol.*, **9**, 115.

CRICK, F. H. C., 1952, *Nature, Lond.*, **170**, 882.

—— 1953, *Acta Cryst.*, **6**, 689.

CRICK, F. H. C., BARNETT, L., BRENNER, S., and WATTS-TOBIN, R. J., 1961, *Nature, Lond.*, **192**, 1227.

CRICK, F. H. C., and RICH, A., 1955, *Nature, Lond.*, **176**, 780.

CRICK, F. H. C., and WATSON, J. D., 1954, *Proc. Roy. Soc.* A, **223**, 80.

CULLIS, A. F., MUIRHEAD, H., PERUTZ, M. F., ROSSMANN, M. G., and NORTH, A. C. T., 1961, *Proc. Roy. Soc.* A, **265**, 15.

—— 1962, *Proc. Roy. Soc.* A, **265**, 161.

Davies, D. R., 1960, *Nature, Lond.*, **186**, 1031.
Dickerson, R. E., Kendrew, J. C., and Strandberg, B. E., 1961, *Computing Methods and the Phase Problem in X-ray Crystal Analysis*, Eds R. Pepinsky, J. M. Robertson and J. C. Speakman (London: Pergamon Press), p. 236.
Dickerson, R. E., Reddy, J. M., Pinkerton, J. M., and Steinrauf, L. K., 1962, *Nature, Lond.*, **196**, 1173.
Dintzis, H. M., 1961, *Proc. Nat. Acad. Sci., Wash.*, **47**, 247.
Feughelman, M., Langridge, R., Seeds, W. E., Stokes, A. R., Wilson, H. R., Hooper, C. W., Wilkins, M. H. F., Barclay, R. K., and Hamilton, L. D., 1955, *Nature, Lond.*, **175**, 834.
Franklin, R. E., and Gosling, R. G., 1953 a, *Acta Cryst.*, **6**, 673.
—— 1953 b, *Nature, Lond.*, **172**, 156.
Franklin, R. E., and Holmes, K. C., 1958, *Acta Cryst.*, **11**, 213.
Franklin, R. E., Klug, A., and Holmes, K. C., 1957, *The Nature of Viruses* (London: Churchill), p. 39.
Fraser, R. D. B., 1953, *J. Chem. Phys.*, **21**, 1511.
Fresco, J. R., Alberts, B. M., and Doty, P., 1960, *Nature, Lond.*, **188**, 98.
Furberg, S., 1950, *Acta Cryst.*, **3**, 325.
Gerald, P. S., and Efron, M. L., 1961, *Proc. Nat. Acad. Sci., Wash.*, **47**, 1758.
Green, D. W., Ingram, V. M., and Perutz, M. F., 1954, *Proc. Roy. Soc.* A, **225**, 287.
Gulland, J. M., and Jordan, D. O., 1947, *Symp. Soc. Exp. Biol.*, **1**, 56.
Harker, D., 1956, *Acta Cryst.*, **9**, 1.
Hodge, A. J., and Schmitt, F. O., 1960, *Proc. Nat. Acad. Sci., Wash.*, **46**, 186.
Hodgkin, D. C., Kamper, J., Lindsey, J., Mackay, M., Pickworth, J., Robertson, J. H., Shoemaker, C. B., White, J. G., Prosen, R. J., and Trueblood, K. N., 1957, *Proc. Roy. Soc.* A, **242**, 228.
Hughes, E. W., 1941, *J. Amer. Chem. Soc.*, **63**, 1737.
Huxley, H. E., and Hanson, E. J., 1960, *Structure and Function of Muscle*, Ed. G. H. Bourne (New York: Academic Press), Vol. 1, Chap. 7.
Huxley, H. E., and Zubay, G., 1960, *J. Mol. Biol.*, **2**, 189.
Kendrew, J. C., Bodo, G., Dintzis, H. M., Parrish, R. G., Wyckoff, H., and Phillips, D. C., 1958, *Nature, Lond.*, **181**, 662.
Kendrew, J. C., Dickerson, R. E., Strandberg, B. E., Hart, R. G., Davies, D. R., Phillips, D. C., and Shore, V. C., 1960, *Nature, Lond.*, **185**, 422.
Kendrew, J. C., Watson, H. C., Strandberg, B. E., Dickerson, R. E., Phillips, D. C., and Shore, V. C., 1961, *Nature, Lond.*, **190**, 666.
Klug, A., and Caspar, D. L. D., 1960, *Advances in Virus Research*, **7**, 225.
Klug, A., and Finch, J. T., 1960, *J. Mol. Biol.*, **2**, 201.
Kraut, J., Sieker, L. C., High, D. F., and Freer, S. T., 1962, *Proc. Nat. Acad. Sci., Wash.*, **48**, 1417.
Kroner, T. D., Tabroff, W., and McGarr, J. J., 1955, *J. Amer. Chem. Soc.*, **77**, 3356.
Langridge, R., Marvin, D. A., Seeds, W. E., Wilson, H. R., Hooper, C. W., Wilkins, M. H. F., and Hamilton, L. D., 1960, *J. Mol. Biol.*, **2**, 38.
Langridge, R., Seeds, W. E., Wilson, H. R., Hooper, C. W., Wilkins, M. H. F., and Hamilton, L. D., 1957, *J. Biophys. Biochem. Cytol.*, **3**, 767.
Langridge, R., Wilson, H. R., Hooper, C. W., Wilkins, M. H. F., and Hamilton, L. D., 1960, *J. Mol. Biol.*, **2**, 19.
Lipson, H., and Cochran, W., 1953, *The Determination of Crystal Structures* (London: Bell).
Meselson, M., and Stahl, F. W., 1958, *Proc. Nat. Acad. Sci., Wash.*, **44**, 671.
Nirenberg, M., and Matthaei, J., 1961, *Proc. Nat. Acad. Sci., Wash.*, **47**, 1588.
Nixon, H. L., and Gibbs, A. J., 1960, *J. Mol. Biol.*, **2**, 197.
North, A. C. T., Cowan, P. M., and Randall, J. T., 1954, *Nature, Lond.*, **174**, 1142.
Patterson, A. L., 1934, *Phys. Rev.*, **46**, 372.
Pauling, L., and Corey, R. B., 1953, *Proc. Roy. Soc.* B, **141**, 21.
Pauling, L., Corey, R. B., and Branson, H. R., 1951, *Proc. Nat. Acad. Sci., Wash.*, **37**, 205.
Perutz, M. F., 1951, *Nature, Lond.*, **167**, 1053.

Perutz, M. F., Rossmann, M. G., Cullis, A. F., Muirhead, H., Will, G., and North, A. C. T., 1960, *Nature, Lond.*, **185**, 416.
Ramachandran, G. N., and Ambady, G. K., 1954, *Curr. Sci.*, **23**, 349.
Ramachandran, G. N., and Kartha, G., 1955, *Nature, Lond.*, **176**, 593.
Rich, A., 1959, *A Symposium on Molecular Biology*, Ed. R. E. Zirkle (Chicago: University of Chicago Press), p. 47.
Rich, A., and Crick, F. H. C., 1955, *Nature, Lond.*, **176**, 915.
—— 1961, *J. Mol. Biol.*, **3**, 483.
Rich, A., Davies, D. R., Crick, F. H. C., and Watson, J. D., 1961, *J. Mol. Biol.*, **3**, 71.
Riley, D. P., and Oster, G., 1951, *Biochim. Biophys. Acta*, **7**, 526.
Robertson, J. M., 1937, *Rep. Progr. Phys.*, **4**, 332 (London: Physical Society).
Robertson, J. M., and Woodward, I., 1940, *J. Chem. Soc.*, 36.
Rossmann, M. G., and Blow, D. M., 1962, *Acta Cryst.*, **15**, 24.
—— 1963, *Acta Cryst.*, **16**, 39.
Schroeder, W. A., Kay, L. M., Legette, J., Honnen, L., and Green, F. C., 1954, *J. Amer. Chem. Soc.*, **76**, 3556.
Spencer, M., 1959, *Acta Cryst.*, **12**, 66.
Spencer, M., Fuller, W., Wilkins, M. H. F., and Brown, G. L., 1962, *Nature, Lond.*, **194**, 1014.
Stanford, R. H., Marsh, R. E., and Corey, R. B., 1962, *Nature, Lond.*, **196**, 1173.
Sutherland, G. B. B. M., Tanner, K. N., and Wood, D. L., 1954, *J. Chem. Phys.*, **22**, 1621.
Watson, J. D., and Crick, F. H. C., 1953, *Nature, Lond.*, **171**, 964.
Wilkins, M. H. F., Gosling, R. G., and Seeds, W. E., 1951, *Nature, Lond.*, **167**, 759.
Wilkins, M. H. F., and Randall, J. T., 1953, *Biochim. Biophys. Acta*, **10**, 192.
Wilkins, M. H. F., Stokes, A. R., and Wilson, H. R., 1953, *Nature, Lond.*, **171**, 737.
Wyatt, G. R., and Cohen, S. S., 1953, *Biochem. J.*, **55**, 774.

X-RAY CRYSTALLOGRAPHY OF LARGE MOLECULES OF BIOLOGICAL IMPORTANCE

A. C. T. North

ADDENDUM

There has been much progress in this field since this article was first published. The structures of several enzymes have now been established at fairly high resolution (2 or 3 Å). These include lysozyme (Blake, Mair, *et al.* 1967), ribonuclease (Wyckoff *et al.* 1967), carboxypeptidase (Reeke *et al.* 1967), chymotrypsin (Matthews *et al.* 1967), and papain (Drenth *et al.* 1968). The structural studies of haemoglobin also have been extended to high resolution (Perutz *et al.* 1968). It now appears that myoglobin and haemoglobin are atypical in having a large proportion of regular (α -helical) structure, linked by short irregular regions; the other proteins studied have a more irregular conformation, and the extended β-conformation is found to be a significant structural feature of globular as well as fibrous proteins. A general structural principle that has emerged from all these studies is the tendency for interior side-chains that are not accessible to the aqueous solvent to be hydrophobic in nature and for the hydrophilic (charged and other polar) side-chains to be confined to surface positions.

With several enzymes it has been found possible to prepare complexes with substrate or inhibitor molecules that form crystals isomorphous with the native enzyme crystals. The positions of the substrate or inhibitor may then be revealed by calculation of a difference electron-density map, for which the coefficients have amplitude given by the difference between the structure amplitudes of the derivative and native crystals and phase equal to that of the native protein. From such studies it has been possible to propose a model for the active mechanism of lysozyme (Blake, Johnson, et al. 1967) which is consistent with chemical studies and which involves a precise juxtaposition of complementary features of enzyme and substrate. The interaction is such that the enzyme binds an intermediate in the reaction, so that it exerts its catalytic effect by favouring the intermediate conformation and hence reducing the energy barrier to the reaction. The reaction mechanism of several other enzymes is in the course of being elucidated in a similar fashion.

REFERENCES

Blake, C. C. F., Mair, G. A., North, A. C. T., *et al.*, 1967, *Proc. R. Soc.* B, **167**, 365.

Blake, C. C. F., Johnson, L. N., Mair, G. A., *et al.*, 1967, *Proc. R. Soc.* B, **167**, 378.

Drenth, J., Jansonius, J. N., Koekoek, R., *et al.*, 1968, *Nature, Lond.*, **218**, 929.

Matthews, B. W., Sigler, P. B., Henderson, R., and Blow, D. M., 1967, *Nature, Lond.*, **214**, 652.

North, A. C. T., and Phillips, D. C., 1968, *Prog. Biophys. Molec. Biol.*, **19** (in press) (Eds. Butler and Noble) (Oxford: Pergamon).

Perutz, M. F., Muirhead, H., Cox, J. M., and Goaman, L. C. G., 1968, Nature, Lond., 219, 131.

Reeke, G. N., Hartsuck, J. A., Ludwig, M. L., et al., 1967, Proc. Natn. Acad. Sci., Wash., 58, 2220.

Wyckoff, H. W., Hardman, K. D., Allewell, N. M., et al., 1967, J. Biol. Chem., 242, 3984.

A. C. T. North
November 1968